THE MARIA THUN
BIODYNAMIC
CALENDAR
2018

CREATED BY
MARIA AND MATTHIAS THUN

Floris
Books

Compiled by Matthias Thun
Translated by Bernard Jarman
Additional astronomical material
by Wolfgang Held and Christian Maclean

Published in German under the title *Aussaattage*
English edition published by Floris Books

British Library CIP Data available

ISBN 978-178250-431-3
ISSN: 2052-5761

Printed in Poland

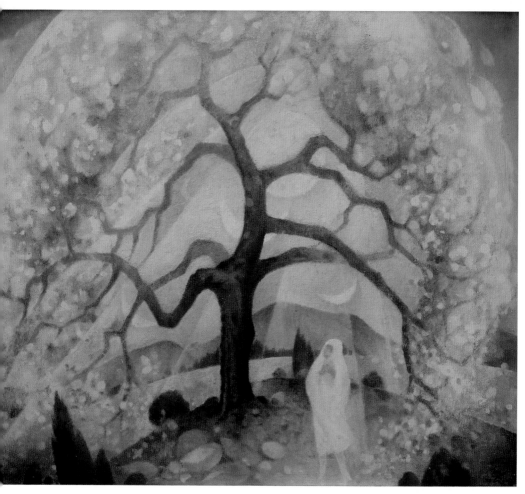

Walter Thun, Flowering Tree, *oil, 59 x 49 cm, 1981*

Walter Thun's *Flowering Tree*

The artist Walter Thun always tried to create his pictures out of a wide and comprehensive background. This painting was inspired by Rudolf Steiner's description of how the biosphere of the earth can be transformed into an organ of the sun by allowing the influence of the planets to work into the minerals of the soil. To stimulate and complete this process the biodynamic preparations are used to help harmonious humus formation. In the diversity of its colours, this picture portrays the working together of Sun, Moon and planets and how their cosmic forces influence this tree.

Introduction

When we were putting together the calendar for 2017 we looked out for planetary aspects that might offer hope for the coming spring, but in vain. We had been spoilt by the springs of 2014 and 2015 and hoped to find something more positive. The spring of 2017 arrived in the way suggested by the planetary aspects – at least in our district. We saw from the weather forecast maps how the northern and southern halves of Germany were experiencing diametrically opposite weather phenomena.

This was different in the early 2000s when we could travel from north to south Germany without experiencing any particular change in the weather. A number of readers observed this change too, but we have unfortunately not been able to give a plausible explanation for it. It seemed the winter never wanted to get going. Our district had about 20 cm (8 in) of snow on two occasions. It lasted only a few days, however, before being replaced by the next mild period. We were pleased to see some hoar frost out on the meadows when we looked out of the window in the early hours but it was usually gone by mid-morning. The only time we had a series of really cold days was when the fruit started to blossom – which we could have done without.

There is an apple tree (Boskoop) which has been growing for more than forty years in a very protected area behind our house and it always gives a good indication of how the fruit is developing generally. The tree bore very few fruit on only two occasions during those forty years. They were years in which, from a planetary point of view, there were no good Fruit aspects. It was very cold this year as blossom time began and the buds started to burst – temperatures ranged from −10° to −14°C (14–7°F) and the frost killed off all but a few flowers that survived at the very top of the tree. The frost layer extended up 4 metres (13 ft) from the ground. The continual rise and fall in temperature was accompanied by very erratic moisture conditions.

It is generally the case that very few pests can survive a long cold winter. If the winter is mild and wet, however, there are likely to be many pests and fungal diseases around in the following spring. In such a scenario the careful choice of fertiliser and plant material can help mitigate some of these challenges. Hardly a week goes by without a reader expressing some frustration about the unsettled weather conditions and turning to us for advice. The treatment of a plant already affected by pests or disease using various teas can only really be effective if the plant has been given the inner strength via the soil to resist any pest attack. To quote Rudolf Steiner in the Agriculture Course: 'The purpose of manuring is to enliven the soil.'

In past years we have often referred to the work of Eleonore Kutschera (from Vienna). She found that during the course of its growth cycle, the plant is able to explore the surrounding soil with its roots and depending on what it finds, use its own plant acids to dissolve mineral substances and make them available. Interestingly, plants grown under biodynamic or organic conditions are better able to do this than plants cultivated for several generations using mineral fertilisers. With the help of such research our understanding of 'fertilisation' can develop in quite a different way. Put simply, it means that farmers and gardeners need to prepare the soil in such a way that every kind of plant will be able to access the substances it needs. Many practitioners would shake their heads in disbelief at such a concept, because they believe that fertiliser must be given to support the crop and not the type of soil.

Manure and Fertiliser

A distinction can be made between organic and mineral or artificial fertilisers. Mineral fertilisers will not be considered here. The following options are available in an organic system:

The 'classic' source of fertility

The classic fertiliser for farming and gardening is animal manure that comes, for example, from cattle, sheep, goats , horses, poultry (hens, ducks, geese) and pigs. In the past these animal manures were collected throughout the year, brought out on the fields in spring or autumn and worked in prior to growing the crops. Thanks to the new understanding of fertility brought about by Justus von Liebig and his nutrient theory, a further aspect was added, namely that of composting animal manure. The composting of manure became increasingly important as new crop varieties were found to suffer from applications of fresh manure because they became susceptible to plant and animal parasites. With the significant change of perception regarding quality during the 1960s and 1970s, an effort was made to find ways of working with animal- and plant-based fertilisers that would not only compete with artificials in terms of yield, but also produce higher quality crops than those grown conventionally. The concept of 'quality', however, often led to huge arguments. It was hard to imagine such a thing as 'good' or 'bad' plant quality extending beyond external appearance and taste.

After Rudolf Steiner had given the course on agriculture in 1924 that laid the foundations for biodynamic agriculture, attempts were made to determine plant quality using not only the techniques of analysis, but also a number of picture-forming methods. That was the start of a very controversial but also highly interesting journey over the following decades: by combining these two approaches it was possible to understand more deeply the concept of quality. Simply relying on visual observation and taste was clearly not enough.

Running parallel to this development were the ever more widespread changes in eating behaviour. People started to eat less meat and were drawn towards a vegetarian diet. This trend led on further towards a vegan lifestyle in which all forms of animal product are avoided. The transition from the prevailing food habits towards vegetarianism has already brought about huge changes. The further step towards a vegan lifestyle, however, is more complicated since our cultivated crop plants can only be grown without animal manures for about five years. Without animal manure, succeeding plant generations will gradually lose their capacity to form the usual fruit.

There is a temptation among vegans to disregard the problem of fertilisation since it is possible to produce plant-based fertilisers and compost to cultivate crops in the short term. In the longer term however this is not possible because the crop plants we have today cannot maintain themselves in such a way. They can be maintained without animal manures for a certain time using mineral fertilisers, but in the long term this would require the development of completely new plants that would have very little in common with our current crops.

In his later years Justus von Liebig acknowledged the shortcomings of his nutrient theory and emphasised that on no account should the care of soil humus be neglected – which depends on compost making. It means that veganism without an animal element of as little as 1%, is not possible.

This discussion, which started with the question of vegetarian food and from there to the issue of a vegan lifestyle, has led to conversations within the biodynamic movement as to whether it is possible to farm without animals. It is not really possible, if we take the Agriculture Course seriously. It may one day be possible as evolution develops, to do without animals altogether, but for biodynamic agriculture this moment has not yet come. The so-called vegetarian preparations are a step in that direction but they are unlikely to replace the animal element completely.

About plant-based compost

In many home gardens no animal manure is used at all. Plant waste, whether from garden or kitchen, is composted and then at a certain moment returned to the earth to release its fertilising effect in the soil. Care should be taken when making this type of plant waste compost however, not to use plant waste on its own but always mix in some garden soil to support a good breakdown process. Lawn mowings play a particularly important role in a home garden. Most gardens have lawns that regularly needs cutting. These mowings have a tendency to go mouldy and interfere with the composting process if they are not mixed with other materials. The mould releases antibiotic substances that prevent a proper humus-forming process.

There are various recommendations about mixing lawn mowings with other materials, such as bark chippings or similar materials, which we would not advise. Bark chippings are very good for keeping areas such as rockeries free from weeds. On areas intended for vegetable growing, however, it is not suitable since the bark used for mulching often comes from timber yards that have been treated with insecticides and fungicides. These would then reappear in the garden soil and make the plants growing in it unfit for human consumption.

It is also important to remember that a bark mulch needs between four and five years to become useful soil. Bark chippings, wood shavings, sawdust and the woody roots of grass and various legume species consist of very durable cellulose fibres in which click beetles like to lay their eggs. Wire worms subsequently emerge from these eggs and can cause a great deal of damage in the vegetable garden as they eat their way through plant roots.

Mixing in some hedge clippings can help prevent the compaction of grass mowings. It is important, however, to avoid any clippings from a thuja hedge since these are very difficult to compost and inhibit the growth of vegetable plants. The same applies to the leaves of walnut trees which are equally difficult to compost.

Making compost with grass cuttings

Comparisons of different composts

Leaf mould and pine needle soil can be fetched from the woods but no great expectations should be placed on it. Many a garden lover has been deeply disappointed after having brought this beautiful, dark woodland soil into the garden believing it to be fine dark humus. The colour of woodland soil has nothing to do with humus. Woodland soil is darker because the carbon compounds are darker due to a lack of movement in the soil. And because this soil comes from a woodland 'monoculture', it doesn't usually provide our cultivated vegetable plants with the living foundations they need.

It is however very good to mix such woodland soil with lawn mowings in order to prevent them matting together and going mouldy. Even so, about 10% should consist of good garden soil or the used earth from a greenhouse – as a kind of cultivated plant inoculation. This mixture, like all composts, should be allowed to rot down for a whole year so that the influences of an entire solar year can work upon it.

When building a compost heap it is important that the base upon which it rests is of garden soil and not meadow soil. A compost heap built on meadow soil takes a long time before it makes a connection with the sub-soil. Only when it has a connection with the sub-soil can it be united with the great sun organ of the earth.

In order to support this connection it is recommended that the work is carried out during transplanting time, the period of the descending moon. However, times which are marked as unfavourable in the calendar should be avoided. Over time, as the compost gradually builds, it is not necessary to observe these finer details. The biodynamic compost preparations and Maria Thun's barrel preparation are then applied to steer the rotting process in the right direction from the very beginning.

It is both a surprise and a delight to experience the many different ways that home gardens are laid out. The eagerness of gardeners and smallholders to try out things is unlimited. A vine may suddenly appear on the veranda or be planted against the garden shed and then be pruned like a rose between autumn and spring so as to produce a wealth of flowers and fruit. However, the vine does not grow equally well everywhere and easily succumbs to mildew. The question then is: Where should we put the diseased prunings? Can they be chopped up and added to the compost? The general rule which every gardener is advised to follow is when fungal growths appear on woody plants like vines and soft fruit, etc., their infected twigs and shoots should be dried out and burnt in a fire bowl or the like because fire will destroy the spores. The ash can then be sprinkled thinly over the compost. Its salt content enhances fertility and has a high manurial value.

About special plant waste composts

Many waste plant materials that arise in the garden during the course of a year can be composted. A certain amount of precision is required of the gardener however when it comes to the separate composting of certain problematic plants. The remains of cruciferous plants for instance should be composted apart. The crucifer family includes most cabbage varieties and also radishes.

When growing members of the cabbage family it is important that they are not grown on the same ground more frequently than every four or five years. The problem with cabbages is that if they are planted too often on the same land, they are likely to be infected with clubroot *(Plasmodiophora brassicae)* which can only be eradicated from the soil if no member of the crucifer family is planted in it for five years. Many gardening books recommend planting mustard as a catch crop, but I believe this to be a highly questionable practice since clubroot can be carried by mustard.

Cabbage waste consists of a lot of leaf but also a great deal of hard stalky material and the woody root ball. The leaves compost easily if kept moist and mixed with some soil. The stems and roots however take a long time to break down and often when a compost heap is opened up after one year, the roots still have a hard skeletal form. It is therefore wise to break up the roots and dry them out. When dried they can be burned and the ash sprinkled over the compost. Gardeners may well shake their heads about this, but it is the surest way of getting rid of any clubroot that may have been unwittingly brought into the garden from the market.

Mixed cultures or companion planting

Many gardeners see great value in growing mixed cultures. The idea is that by growing different plant species together, pests that might affect one are kept away by the scents of another species. This has, however, one major disadvantage. If we want to use the Moon constellations to support the crops, we need to be able to address the impulses of the Root, Leaf, Flower or Fruit.

If we have a row of carrots, a row of lettuce and one of paprika, then the lettuce will have long been harvested by the time the paprikas and carrots reach maturity. The lettuce thrives when it is hoed and cared for at Leaf times. Doing so however, means that the carrots will also be affected and they would prefer to be hoed at Root times. And on the other side we find the paprika which would rather be hoed at a Fruit time. This means either leaving a lot of space between the rows or treating some of the plants at a less favourable moment. To overcome this problem it is worth planting the various vegetable varieties each on their own bed or in rows with an adequate distance to their neighbours. A description follows (opposite) of a crop rotation which has proved its worth for many years and was recommended by Maria Thun.

Animal pests and compost

Whenever animal pests make an appearance in the garden, we hope to get rid of them using certain herb teas. By then it is often too late because the pests usually arrive when the plants are growing in a soil that does not suit them. The subsequent application of teas is therefore only an emergency solution.

The best thing is either to use special composts or apply the tea to the soil when the seed bed is being created so that the plants can grow and thrive in the soil prepared for them. It is of course not possible to make a special compost for all the different plants. In order to prepare the ground for certain species in a tree nursery for instance, special composts of, say, oak or beech leaves can be used in order to prepare them for the conditions they will meet out in the woods. Since this would be impractical in a garden situation it is important that the compost is able to mature for a whole year. This will allow the constellations of an entire solar year to work upon it.

Afterwards, the compost needs to be spread at the right time. This usually means spreading it in autumn and then working it into the soil so that the spring sowing can begin at the right moment. This general rule can also be adapted to a greenhouse situation.

The most universal of plant composts is that made from stinging nettles. On page 14 a description is given of the many ways in which nettles can be used both as compost and a fertiliser as well as a cultivation tool.

Gardening without fertiliser

If the many possibilities and pitfalls connected with fertility and manuring in the garden faze gardeners and cause them to hang their head in despair, there is also a possibility of fertilising without using a fertiliser. Most fertilisers are applied in order to prepare the soil for the plants and to ensure the plants yield well. There is, however, a fertiliser that can neither be seen, smelt nor purchased but which depends on the gardener being active. And this fertiliser is the air.

A major part of the air consists of nitrogen, and nitrogen is one of the most interesting of horticultural fertilisers. If the soil around the plants is loosened with a hoe or rake once a week, a lot of nitrogen from the air can be brought into the soil, especially if it is done at the right time and in accord with their fruiting type. Hoeing of course means that soil organisms are being destroyed, and because of this some people object to such cultivation practices. But it also means that the micro-organisms in the soil's surface layer become more active, are able to fix nitrogen from the air and make it available to the plants in a very accessible and plant-friendly form, a form that ensures healthy growth and can never result in over-fertilisation.

Some people unfortunately recommend never hoeing the soil so as not to destroy any micro-organisms. In order to draw benefit from them, however, it is necessary to 'annoy' them a little, get them to orientate themselves differently and enable the plants to take up new life forces from the earth.

Crop Rotation

Maria Thun

The image of the ideal crop rotation is expressed as a cropping sequence based on the fivefold fruiting possibilities of the plant itself – root, flower, leaf, seed, fruit. This sequence is found in the orientation of cosmic impulses that emanate from the zodiac. The crop rotation may be experienced as an organism with each of its constituent parts as organs that relate to organ systems of the human being.

Rudolf Steiner refers to this in a way that always reminds me of a crop rotation. The reference to the human being appears as he discusses the relationship between the plant and the human being, where the plant substances take effect and from where they originate – from the root to the nerve and brain system, the leaf to the lungs, the flower to the kidney system, the fruit to the blood and the seed to the system of the human heart. If we then look at the various cosmic rhythms we will discover an extraordinary relationship between the various conjunctions of Venus and the Sun in our century.

Conjunctions take place in five positions about 72° apart from one another and shift only very slowly – only around 30° in the course of a century. At the present time conjunctions occur in the constellations of Taurus–Earth–brain, Sagittarius–Fruit–blood, Leo–Seed–heart, Pisces–Leaf–lung, Libra–Flower–kidney and back again to Taurus just a few degrees further on. The picture overleaf is a schematic diagram of these conjunction positions in the zodiac.

It seems to me that by taking such relationships into consideration our plants would be able to nourish the human being and its system of organs in the right way. During the course of a single year, these five basic crop types can be present as a cropping sequence on the various garden plots and fields. Rudolf Steiner spoke to farmers and gardeners about an individualised organism existing through time and I believe that it can be realised by developing such a crop rotation.

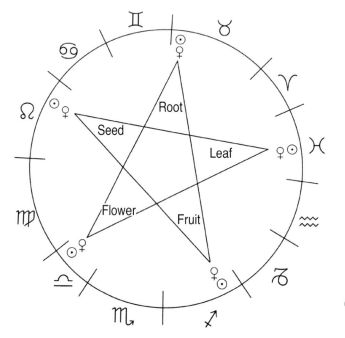

In recent decades the move towards farming without livestock has led to an excessive emphasis being placed on cereals in the rotation. This in turn has led to fungal problems and an increased use of plant protection chemicals. Increasing pressure is being placed on crop rotations today, not only because of the vagaries of soil and climate but because of the machinery required. This is why each farm needs to develop its own approach. A crop rotation can present gardeners and smallholders with a problem, however. A number of crops have very short growing cycles, often only a few weeks with one crop succeeding another in great rapidity. Unless everything is written down, the gardener soon loses track and by the end of the season everything is mixed up.

The soil is depleted in a one-sided way if the same species is grown too frequently on the same spot. Deficiencies begin to appear and plants become less productive. Pests and diseases then start appearing as a direct result of our inattentiveness. Even if we succeed in keeping the plants alive using various counter measures, their quality will be compromised.

Consider for a moment the vegetables in the crucifer family. They appear in the most varied of forms. The strength of growth in the cabbage varieties is held back with leaf upon leaf being pressed close together to form a fruiting organ in the leaf region of the plant. In other varieties the root collar swells up, as with radishes and turnips. Brussels sprouts create 'fruits' along the stem, while the stem of kohlrabi thickens to produce a tasty delicacy; then there is the cauliflower formed in the heart of the plant. Each of these fruiting organs requires particular forces which on the one hand make certain demands on the soil, and on the other leave potentially burdensome residues behind.

After one growing season it is not only these brassica plants that are exhausted, but also the forces that enable their fruiting organs to develop. This means that not only must another plant family occupy the ground the following year, but another kind of fruiting organ must be developed too. An example of a possible crop rotation for vegetables is presented below, one which has proved its value over many years.

In the absence of any more neutral options, an ageing strawberry bed can be chosen as a starting point. After the harvest the plantation is ploughed and sown down with rye and Persian clover. Because soils need a regular period of grass growth, it is very helpful to plant rye. In the autumn these plants are then turned in lightly during a descending moon period and sprayed up to three times with barrel preparation (cow pat pit, CPP). It goes without saying that the individual crop species will need treating with special composts prior to their being sown or planted. Plots no longer needed in the autumn are dug over for the winter.

Soil cultivation trials carried out for over 25 years at the University of Giessen by Professor von Boguslawski and Dr Debruck have shown that the traditional practice of digging or ploughing the soil in the autumn ready for winter, produces the best results in terms of soil fertility as compared with other more recent practices.

The recommended cropping sequence for the first year

Plot 1	Plot 2	Plot 3	Plot 4	Plot 5
White cabbage	Carrots	Peas	Potatoes	Strawberries
Red cabbage	Parsnips	Broad beans	Potatoes	Strawberries
Savoy	Salsify	Sugar peas	Potatoes	Strawberries
Cauliflower	Beetroot	Dwarf beans	Broccoli	Strawberries
Curly kale	Onions	Sweetcorn	Broccoli	Strawberries
Brussels sprouts	Celery	Runner beans	J'salem artichokes	Strawberries
Kohlrabi	Leeks	Peppers	J'salem artichokes	Strawberries
Turnips	Chard	Cucumbers	J'salem artichokes	Strawberries
Radish	Fennel	Tomatoes	J'salem artichokes or Flowers	Strawberries
Winter radish	Parsley	Gherkins	Flowers	Strawberries

In the following years the crops are changed. Spinach, lettuce, corn salad, fat hen and endive can be grown as pre or catch crops. They are not so dependent on the crop rotation but should not follow one another and be planted on the same ground in one year. A light dose of compost should be given when successional sowings are carried out.

Nettles

Maria Thun

Using stinging nettles

Stinging nettle *(Urtica dioica)* is used as one of the biodynamic compost preparations once it has undergone a special fermentation process. There are also a number of other ways to use it for controlling pests and stimulating growth.

a) The 24-hour extract

About 1 kg (2 lb) of fresh nettles (without roots), which may be in flower but have not yet gone to seed, are placed within a container made of wood, clay or a material coated with enamel. It is then covered in 10 litres (10 quarts) of cold or hand warm water and left to stand for twenty-four hours. The carefully sieved extract is then used as a spray where grubs and caterpillars are a problem. It should be sprayed three times within a few hours.

Pit where nettles remain for a year

It is covered with turf and soil and well marked

Stinging nettle compost frame with spruce covering

Production of the 24-hour extract

b) Stinging nettle brew as a growth stimulant

The solution is made in the same way as that just described, but is then left to stand until at least the leaves have decomposed in the water. This may be after three or four days or several weeks, depending on the ambient temperature. The term liquid manure (Jauche) is used because the liquid has a smell similar to that of liquid animal manure.

It has a powerful manuring effect and must therefore be considerably diluted before being applied. When sprayed on the soil it is diluted 1:10 with water. When used for watering it should be diluted 1:40. If, as a result of a cold spell of weather, there is a check in growth which often draws in aphids, this dilution ratio can be used. The spraying should be undertaken towards evening or in the early morning to stimulate growth and help the plants overcome their shock. It is important, however, to give water afterwards because the liquid manure stimulates the plant to such an extent that the normal moisture is insufficient and they will tend to wilt. It has been found that when roses, soft fruit, apple trees, etc., have been given this treatment three times in succession, the flow of sap improves and aphids, and frequently fungal problems too, disappear.

c) General support of plant growth

The starting point for this brew is the same as that described under (a) and the way it is produced accords with (b) but the brew concentration is reduced.

A quarter litre (8 fl oz) of brew is added to 10 litres (10 quarts) of water and watered on crops like tomatoes, cucumbers, spinach, cabbage, etc. Alternatively

Production of stinging nettle brew

Brew after 4 weeks, and 24-hour extract (right)

half a litre of brew is stirred for 15 minutes in 10 litres of water and then sprayed out as a mist over the beds. Potatoes benefit from this in particular and if soft fruit bushes are sprayed after the fruit has been picked, the effect will be visible the following year.

Whichever approach is chosen, it is important that no more than three treatments are given, otherwise quality is likely to suffer. It will show itself in terms of reduced keeping quality and a decline in germination capacity. This is especially true if the brew is applied in a more concentrated form than recommended here.

d) Stinging nettle compost
Compost made entirely of stinging nettles produces the ideal soil for raising delicate crops and for cultivating roses and strawberries. Only a successful spruce needle compost comes anywhere near it.

Maria Thun working in her fields

Sowing on Good Friday and Holy Saturday

Matthias Thun

Trials carried out 35 or 40 years ago and repeated many times since then have shown that Good Friday and Holy Saturday cannot be recommended for sowing or transplanting. Seeds sown on those days germinate poorly, produce weak seedlings and result in poor yields. Young plants that are transplanted on these days don't root properly, their leaves hang down and most of them don't survive. This negative effect on plant growth begins in the early morning of Good Friday and ends at sunrise on Easter Sunday. This is why these times have been marked as unfavourable in the calendar every year.

In the last few years planetary oppositions have occurred on these days, bringing with them fine weather and good soil conditions. Sometimes the weather after Easter was no longer so good. Gardeners then complained because they couldn't make use of the fine days.

Some years ago, on one particular Good Friday there was a planetary opposition and on Holy Saturday, a Warmth trine. The soil was in an excellent condition and the weather perfect for sowing grain. We therefore decided to sow three different grains – spring rye, spring wheat and naked barley. The area chosen covered 1 000 square metres. A light application of compost had been given the previous autumn. Everything was sown at the same time. It was then subsequently divided up to compare different hoeing and spraying times. If the sowing date proved unfavourable we wanted to find out which cosmic impulses could be used to assist growth when hoeing and applying preparations. Apart from the necessary headlands we worked with five variants:

1. 0 – Control
2. AK was hoed and sprayed with horn silica at Leaf times
3. WK was hoed and sprayed with horn silica at Fruit times
4. EK was hoed and sprayed with horn silica at Root times
5. LK was hoed and sprayed with horn silica at Flower times

Each variant was repeated three times. Horn manure was given three times at the time of sowing. The moon was in Sagittarius, a Fruit time.

The seeds germinated very quickly, so we assumed that things would be different this year. But the plants soon became stunted, they struggled to grow beyond the seedling stage, were very late in shooting and it seemed that they wouldn't produce any ears. In the end some meagre ears were produced. The crop was hoed and sprayed regularly but the sight of the crop could make one weep. When harvest time arrived, the corn didn't ripen. The grains didn't get hard despite there being so few of them. Then the rain came. After two weeks a day came when the sky cleared. The grain had become no riper, but those of the Leaf time variant had already started sprouting. Everything was then threshed and further dried. Already while carrying it in we noticed how the weight varied. When it was dry the yields were as follows (100 kg/ha):

Variant	Control	AK: Leaf	WK: Fruit	EK: Root	LK: Flower
Naked Barley	14.00	18.64	19.68	17.68	18.40
Spring rye	33.00	29.80	42.00	36.50	36.00
Spring wheat	22.40	25.40	38.00	28.00	30.00

The controls were hoed at Fruit times but not treated three times with horn silica. The yields were low. In the case of rye and wheat, the effect of horn silica at Leaf times went into the straw and increased its mass while the barley saw an increase in grain. All three grains responded best to Fruit time cultivations.

This shows once again that poor quality caused by the choice of sowing time can be significantly improved by choosing favourable times for soil cultivation. Good Friday and Holy Saturday, however, will continue to be marked as unfavourable in the calendar. (It is worth noting that unlike other effects which have to be converted from GMT to local time, this effect is always in local time.)

Whenever the weather is fine and sunny on Good Friday and Holy Saturday and the soil is dry, we always receive letters from discontented farmers and gardeners who have little understanding for these unfavourable times in the calendar. When reading such letters memories come streaming back to me. It was my pleasure to look after a biodynamic group in Marburg for 25 years. We met each Monday evening and in the winter we studied what we were practising during summer. In the summer we spent Monday evenings visiting each other's gardens or farms. One of those we visited was Egenolf von Schenk. He raised vegetable seedlings for us all in his garden.

One day he arrived most upset and said that hundreds of celery seedlings which he had pricked out on Holy Saturday had withered after a few days. We couldn't explain why this happened but we had a hunch. That is why we decided to carry out many sowing trials the following year on those days. That year many small gardeners agreed to sow different kinds of seeds each day from Maundy Thursday through to Easter Monday. When we visited each other in the summer we looked to see what had happened with the various sowings. In most cases the plants sown on Good Friday and Holy Saturday were weak, beset by pests or had died. The trials were repeated several years running and each time there was a similar result.

In ancient cultures when people still lived strongly with the forces of nature, the spring Full Moon was the time of mourning for the death of Baldur, Osiris and other gods. On the Sunday that followed they experienced the resurrection of those gods out in nature. The Crucifixion and Resurrection of Christ followed these ancient laws. The event which occurred nearly two thousand years ago between the sun and the earth continues to leave its mark on the earth each year at Easter time.

Potato Cultivation

Matthias Thun

Recommendations for potato cultivation always used to begin with an application of manure in spring time. The generally held opinion was that the manure applied should be as fresh as possible so as to force strong growth. After more than forty years of potato trials and working with all manner of cultivation methods we have found time and again that potatoes are healthiest if 15 tonnes/ha (7 tons/acre) of well composted manure is spread on the land the previous autumn. The compost is mixed into the surface layer preferably during the descending Moon in October. Barrel preparation is sprayed at the same time. After about four weeks, but at the latest by mid-November, plough the field for the winter.

In November the soil organisms increase in number and become active in the soil. If ploughing is delayed till December, their work is disturbed. The soil will then no longer be transformed and there is a danger of nutrients leaching out into the ground water.

In spring the soil is worked with a cultivator and harrowed. Each time it is cultivated, horn manure is sprayed and the potatoes are planted at Root times. Because potatoes love to feel air around their roots they are hoed twice at Root times along with a spraying of horn silica. When they are hoed and sprayed for the third time they are also earthed up so that the potatoes don't turn green.

In areas where potato blight is a problem, stinging nettle tea can be sprayed up to three times in the evening. Cover 1 kg of green leaf matter with about 5 litres (2 lb to 5 quarts) of cold water and then bring it to the boil. The tea is then mixed with 100 litres (25 gal) of water and sprayed as a fine mist over the potatoes. This strengthens the leaves and keeps the plants healthy.

Propagating potatoes from seed

In very warm years potatoes can develop seeds. The fruits containing the seed hang down from the plants like tomatoes. Up to sixty years ago these fruits would turn yellow before harvest. Today they must be harvested green and allowed to ripen afterwards. The fruits are then cut open and the many seeds then dried. They can be sown like tomatoes in the greenhouse or in a pot on the window sill of a warm room.

The best moment to choose is the last Root time while the Sun is in Capricorn (first half of February). In comparison trials we have found Capricorn to have the best results. As soon as the plants have two seed leaves they are pricked out into modules or blocks. The potting compost is sprayed with horn manure and then thoroughly mixed. By the middle of May they will be about 12 to 15 cm (4–6 in) and can be planted outside and treated in the same way as the potatoes described earlier. When harvested in the autumn they become the seed potatoes for the following year's crop.

Propagating from eyes

In order to regenerate the potato, Rudolf Steiner recommended taking and planting the middle eyes of the potato. After years of trialling different aspects and constellations we have found the Moon in Aries to be the most suitable for potato eyes. The middle eyes of the potato are cut out about 1 to 2 cm (½–1 in) in size as if peeling the potato. They are then planted with the cut edge in the soil 3 cm (1 in) deep and 10 cm (4 in) apart when the Moon is in Aries.

All cultivation work is best carried out with the Moon in Aries. Relatively small potatoes are harvested which are then used for cropping the following year. They are then planted and cultivated at Root times.

Cutting the eye of the potato

Potato fruits

Potato trials

Planting in Aries to regenerate potatoes

The rejuvenation of potatoes can be achieved with good results and without any specialised procedures if from time to time seed potatoes are planted when the Moon is in Aries. Tubers should of course only be used that weigh no more than 35 g (1¼ oz). The potatoes will not grow very large but they will be ideal for planting out the following year. Subsequent cultivation work and horn silica applications should also be carried out when the Moon is in Aries.

Research results

There follows a research report about a crop of potatoes originating from seeds collected in 1990. The seeds were sown for the first time in the way described and then planted out. In 1992 the potatoes were planted in when the Moon was in the same constellation as that from which the seeds came. For reasons of space we were only able to plant four variants. The aim was to compare different planting times and three corresponding applications of horn silica. A control was also planted for each variant to which no silica preparation was applied. There were thus 8 variants in all. In 1993 the resulting tubers were planted out and cultivated as a single crop in the way described earlier. Of each variant 150 tubers (weighing between 30 and 35 grams, 1–1¼ oz) were planted. Planting was carried out at Root times along with three applications of horn manure. After being earthed up they were hoed three times and simultaneously treated with horn silica preparation. The resulting yields (in 100 kg/ha) of the follow-on crop from 1992 were as follows:

Constellation of planting time	Control yield	Yield with horn silica
Virgo (Root time)	467	492
Libra (Flower time)	441	467
Scorpio (Leaf time)	428	447
Sagittarius (Fruit time)	387	395

It should again be emphasised that in 1993 the same optimal measures were applied throughout. The differences brought about by the horn silica in 1992 improved the quality of seed. The experience of many years has shown that propagation from seed offers a real future for potatoes grown under biodynamic conditions.

Comments regarding the cultivation and consumption of potatoes

Like the tomato and pepper, the potato is a member of the nightshade family. It has been grown in Europe since the mid-seventeenth century. It was initially considered to be an ornamental plant with its strong leaves and fine flowers. From these then come the berry-like fruits which, like the tomato, contain a large number of seeds. These fruits are of course inedible. They can, however, be used to develop new varieties.

In its natural state the potato is very robust and needs around 100 days from planting to harvest. This period refers to the time potato tubors require to grow from the roots in the earth and which through cultivation of the former ornamental plant, become the potatoes we consume today. The potato has steadily spread to become a staple food over much of the earth.

Rudolf Steiner also brought new impulses to the subject of nutrition. He could see that one-sided nutrition reduces the capacity of human beings to think creatively. He also pointed out that changes in the health status of the body have their origin in the food we eat. He described how the organs of metabolism through which the potato passes are not able to create any substance from the potato to support the brain and nervous system. Its digestion comes to an end there. Instead of developing a capacity for free thinking, the potato has a dumbing-down effect.

Because so many potatoes were being consumed at the beginning of the twentieth century, he recommended bringing cereals such as rye, wheat, barley and oats more strongly into the food chain. So long as they have been cooked or gone through a process of baking, cereals are sufficiently ready for the human metabolism to completely transform them before passing substance to the brain and nervous system.

Dr Gerhard Schmidt and Dr Udo Renzenbrink, two anthroposophic nutritionists, dedicated much of their lives to researching the nutritional value of cereals for human food. They were then very surprised to discover that Maria Thun had placed so much importance on the quality of potatoes. After the first ten years of her research (there were about 45 years in all), they compared the quality of potatoes with that of cereals. The potato was never Maria Thun's favourite crop, but because so many people had it on their daily menu she felt that for the sake of their health it should be cultivated in the best way possible. A sufficient number of potato samples were therefore made available and Gerhard Schmidt and Udo Renzenbrink set about using their experience to assess their quality. They had samples of potatoes grown at Root, Leaf, Flower and Fruit times which had been treated according to standard biodynamic practices.

Chemical analyses were made at every stage of the research. All the samples were also investigated using picture building methods – it was a mammoth task. Students were used as volunteers. The individual steps were:

— The raw potato was examined
— The cooked potato was examined
— The taste of different samples was evaluated (Leaf time potatoes tasted so bad that no student wanted to test them)
— Both the raw and the cooked potatoes were also chewed
— Both the raw and cooked potato was swallowed
— After some time they were retrieved from the stomach
— Finally, following an agreed period to digest them, the students were asked to solve mathematical problems in order to test their thinking capacity

It was already known that the consumption of roots – the potato is strictly speaking not a root – such as beetroot, turnips and carrots give support to mathematical thinking. The end result surprised everyone involved. The Root time potatoes treated with horn silica and especially the Capricorn potatoes gave the best results. They had the best flavour, gave the best analytical results and images in the picture-building methods and in terms of supporting thinking capacity, mathematical problem solving compared favourably to that of cereals.

These intensive investigations led to life-long mutual recognition of the work carried out by Gerhard Schmidt, Udo Renzenbrink and Maria Thun. It also showed that by making use of cosmic influences together with the biodynamic preparations, true quality can be achieved.

Background to the Calendar

The zodiac

The **zodiac** is a group of twelve constellations of stars which the Sun, Moon and all the planets pass on their circuits. The Sun's annual path always takes exactly the same line, called **ecliptic**. The Moon's and planets' paths vary slightly, sometimes above and sometimes below the ecliptic. The point at which their paths cross the ecliptic is called a **node** (☊ and ☋).

The angles between the Sun, Moon and planets are called **aspects.** In this calendar the most important is the 120° angle, or **trine.**

In the illustration below the outer circle shows the varying sizes of the visible **constellations** of the **zodiac**. The dates on this outer circle are the days on which the Sun enters the constellation (this can change by one day because of leap years). The inner circle shows the divisions into equal sections of 30° corresponding to the **signs** used in astrology.

It is the *constellations,* not the signs, on which our observations are based, and which are used throughout this calendar.

The twelve constellations are grouped into four different types, each having three constellations at an angle of about 120°, or trine. About every nine days the Moon passes from one type, for instance Root, through the other types (Flower, Leaf and Fruit) and back to Root again.

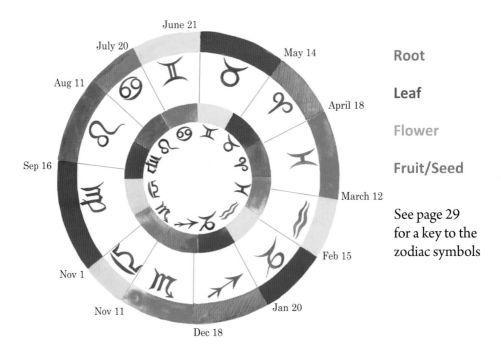

Root

Leaf

Flower

Fruit/Seed

See page 29 for a key to the zodiac symbols

If a New Moon is at a node there is a solar eclipse, as the Moon is directly in front of the Sun, while a Full Moon at a node causes a lunar eclipse where the Earth's shadow falls on the Moon. If the Sun or Moon pass exactly in front of a planet, there is an occultation (●). If Mercury or Venus pass exactly in front of the Sun, this is a transit (other planets cannot pass in front of the Sun).

What are oppositions, trines and conjunctions?
Oppositions ☍

A **geocentric** (Earth-centred) **opposition** occurs when for the observer on the Earth there are two planets opposite one another – 180° apart – in the heavens. They look at one another from opposite sides of the sky and their light interpenetrates. Their rays fall onto the Earth and stimulate in a beneficial way the seeds that are being sown in that moment. In our trials we have found that seeds sown at times of opposition resulted in a higher yield of top quality crops.

With a **heliocentric** (Sun-centred) **opposition** an observer would need to place themselves on the Sun. This is of course physically impossible but we can understand it through our thinking. The Sun is in the centre and the two planets placed 180° apart also gaze at each other but this time across the Sun. Their rays are also felt by the Earth and stimulate better plant growth. However, heliocentric oppositions are not shown or taken into account in the calendar.

At times of opposition two zodiac constellations are also playing their part. If one planet is standing in a Warmth constellation, the second one will usually be in a Light constellation or vice versa. If one planet is in a Water constellation, the other will usually be in an Earth one. (As the constellations are not equally sized, the point opposite may not always be in the opposite constellation.)

Trines △ or ▲

The twelve constellations are grouped into four different types, each having three constellations at an angle of about 120°, or trine. About every nine days the Moon passes a similar region of forces.

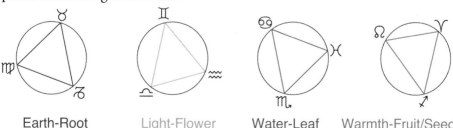

| Earth-Root | Light-Flower | Water-Leaf | Warmth-Fruit/Seed |

Trines occur when planets are 120° from one another. The two planets are then usually both standing in the same elemental configuration – Aries and Leo for example, are both Warmth constellations. A Warmth trine means that the effects of these constellations will enhance fruit and seed formation in the plants sown at this time. If two planets are in trine position in Water, watery influences will be enhanced, which usually brings high rainfall. Plants sown on these days will yield more leaf than those on other days. Trine effects can change the way plants grow.

Conjunctions ♂

Conjunctions and multiple conjunctions occur when two or more planets stand behind one another in space. It is then usually only the planet closest to the Earth that has any influence on plant growth. If this influence is stronger than that of the sidereal Moon, cosmic disturbances can occur that irritate the plant and cause checks in growth. This negative effect is increased further when the Moon or another planet stands directly in front of another – an occultation (•) or eclipse in the case of Sun and Moon. Sowing at these times will affect subsequent growth detrimentally and harm a plant's regenerative power.

The effects of the Moon

In its 27-day orbit round the Earth, the Moon passes through the constellations of the zodiac and transmits forces to the Earth which affect the four elements: Earth, Light (Air), Water and Warmth (Fire). They in turn affect the four parts of the plant: the roots, the flower, the leaves and the fruit or seeds. The health and growth of a plant can therefore be stimulated by sowing, cultivating and harvesting it in tune with the cycles of the Moon.

These cosmic forces can also be harnessed in beekeeping. By opening and closing the bee 'skep' or box in rhythm with the Moon, the bees' activity is directly affected.

The table opposite summarises the effects of the movement of the Moon through the twelve constellations on plants, bees and the weather.

The amount of time the Moon spends in any constellation varies between two and four days. However, this basic framework can be disrupted by planetary oppositions which override the normal tendencies; equally, it may be that trine positions (see above) activate a different elemental force to the ones the Moon is transmitting. Times when the Moon's path or a planet's path intersects with the ecliptic (ascending ☊ or descending ☋ node; see page 24) are subject to mainly negative effects. These are intensified if there is an eclipse or occultation, in which case the nearer planet interrupts the influence of the distant one. Such days are unsuitable for sowing or harvesting.

Constellation	Sign	Element	Plant	Bees	Weather
Pisces, Fishes	♓ W	Water	Leaf	Making honey	Damp
Aries, Ram	♈ H	Warmth	Fruit	Gathering nectar	Warm/hot
Taurus, Bull	♉ E	Earth	Root	Building comb	Cool/cold
Gemini, Twins	♊ L	Light	Flower	Gathering pollen	Airy/bright
Cancer, Crab	♋ W	Water	Leaf	Making honey	Damp
Leo, Lion	♌ H	Warmth	Fruit	Gathering nectar	Warm/hot
Virgo, Virgin	♍ E	Earth	Root	Building comb	Cool/cold
Libra, Scales	♎ L	Light	Flower	Gathering pollen	Airy/bright
Scorpio, Scorpion	♏ W	Water	Leaf	Making honey	Damp
Sagittarius, Archer	♐ H	Warmth	Fruit	Gathering nectar	Warm/hot
Capricorn, Goat	♑ E	Earth	Root	Building comb	Cool/cold
Aquarius, Waterman	♒ L	Light	Flower	Gathering pollen	Airy/bright

Groupings of plants for sowing and harvesting

When we grow plants, different parts are cultivated for food. We can divide them into four groups.

Root crops at Root times

Radishes, swedes, sugar beet, beetroot, celeriac, carrot, scorzonera, etc., fall into the category of root plants. Potatoes and onions are included in this group too. Root times produce good yields and top storage quality for these crops.

Leaf plants at Leaf times

The cabbage family, lettuce, spinach, lambs lettuce, endive, parsley, leafy herbs and fodder plants are categorised as leaf plants. Leaf times are suitable for sowing and tending these plants but not for harvesting and storage. For this (as well as harvesting of cabbage for sauerkraut) Fruit and Flower times are recommended.

Flower plants at Flower times

These times are favourable for sowing and tending all kinds of flower plants but also for cultivating and spraying 501 (a biodynamic preparation) on oil-bearing plants such as linseed, rape, sunflower, etc. Cut flowers have the strongest scent and remain fresh for longer if cut at Flower times, and the mother plant will provide many new side shoots. If flowers for drying are harvested at Flower times they retain the most vivid colours. If cut at other times they soon lose their colour. Oil-bearing plants are best harvested at Flower times.

Fruit Plants at Fruit times

Plants that are cultivated for their fruit or seed belong to this category, including beans, peas, lentils, soya, maize, tomatoes, cucumber, pumpkin, zucchini, but also cereals for summer and winter crops. Sowing oil-bearing plants at Fruit times provides the best yields of seeds. The best time for extraction of oil later on is at Flower times. Leo times are particularly suitable to grow good seed. Fruit plants are best harvested at Fruit times. They store well and their seeds provide good plants for next year. When storing fruit, also remember to choose the time of the ascending Moon.

There is always uncertainty as to which category some plants belong (see list on p. 57). Onions and beetroot provide a similar yield when sown at Root and Leaf times, but the keeping quality is best from Root times. Kohlrabi and cauliflowers belong to Leaf times, as does Florence fennel. Broccoli is more beautiful and firmer when sown at Flower times.

Explanations of the Calendar Pages

Next to the date is the constellation (and time of entry) in which the Moon is positioned. This is the astronomical constellation, not the astrological sign (see page 24). The next column shows solar and lunar events.

A further column shows which element is dominant on that day (this is useful for beekeepers). Note H is used for warmth (heat). Sometimes there is a change during the day; in this case, both elements are mentioned. Warmth effects on thundery days are implied but are not mentioned in this column, but may have a ϟ symbol in the far right 'Weather' column.

The next column shows in colour the part of the plant which will be enhanced by sowing or cultivation on that day. Numbers indicate times of day. On the extreme right, special events in nature are noted as well as anticipated weather changes which disturb or break up the overall weather pattern.

When parts of the plant are indicated that do not correspond to the Moon's position in the zodiac (often it is more than one part on the same day), it is not a misprint, but takes account of other cosmic aspects which overrule the Moon-zodiac pattern and have an effect on a different part of the plant.

Unfavourable times are marked thus ▬. These are caused by eclipses, nodal points of the Moon or the planets or other aspects with a negative influence; they are not elaborated upon in the calendar. If one has to sow at unfavourable times for practical reasons, one can choose favourable days for hoeing, which will improve the plant.

The position of the planets in the zodiac is shown in the box below, with the date of entry into a new constellation. R indicates the planet is moving retrograde (with the date when retrograde begins), D indicates the date when it moves in direct motion again.

On the opposite calendar page astronomical aspects are indicated. Those visible to the naked eye are shown in **bold** type. Visible conjunctions (particularly Mercury's) are not always visible from all parts of the Earth.

Astronomical symbols

Constellations		Planets		Aspects			
♓	Pisces	☉	Sun	☊	Ascending node	**St**	Storms likely
♈	Aries	☾, ☽	Moon	☋	Descending node	⚡	Thunder likely
♉	Taurus	☿	Mercury	⌢	Highest Moon	**Eq**	Earthquakes
♊	Gemini	♀	Venus	⌣	Lowest Moon	**Tr**	Traffic dangers
♋	Cancer	♂	Mars	**Pg**	Perigee	**Vo**	Volcanic activity
♌	Leo	♃	Jupiter	**Ag**	Apogee		
♍	Virgo	♄	Saturn	☍	Opposition		Northern Transplanting Time
♎	Libra	♅	Uranus	☌	Conjunction		
♏	Scorpio	♆	Neptune	•	Eclipse/occultation		Southern Transplanting Time
♐	Sagittarius	♇	Pluto	•̷	Lunar eclipse		
♑	Capricorn	○	Full Moon	△	Trine (or ▲)		
♒	Aquarius	●	New Moon	E Earth L Light/Air W Water H Warmth/Heat			

Transplanting times

From midwinter through to midsummer the Sun rises earlier and sets later each day while its path across the sky ascends higher and higher. From midsummer until midwinter this is reversed, the days get shorter and the midday Sun shines from an ever lower point in the sky. This annual ascending and descending of the Sun creates our seasons. As it ascends and descends during the course of the year the Sun is slowly moving (from an Earth-centred point of view) through each of the twelve constellations of the zodiac in turn. On average it shines for one month from each constellation.

In the northern hemisphere the winter solstice occurs when the Sun is in the constellation of Sagittarius and the summer solstice when it is in Gemini. At any point from Sagittarius to Gemini the Sun is ascending, while from Gemini to Sagittarius it is descending. In the southern hemisphere this is reversed.

The Moon (and all the planets) follow approximately the same path as the Sun

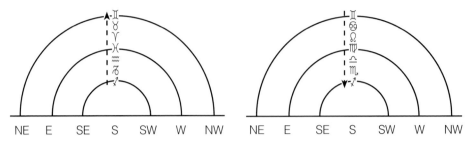

Northern hemisphere ascending Moon (left) and descending Moon (right): Transplanting Time

around the zodiac but instead of a year, the Moon takes only about 27 ½ days to complete one cycle, shining from each constellation in turn for a period of two to three days. This means that the Moon will ascend for about fourteen days and then descend.

It is important to distinguish the journey of the Moon through the zodiac (siderial rhythm) from the waxing and waning (synodic) cycle: in any given constellation there may be a waxing, waning, full, quarter, sickle or gibbous Moon. As it moves through the zodiac the Moon, like the Sun, is ascending (in the northern hemisphere) when it is in the constellations from Sagittarius to Gemini and descending from Gemini to Sagittarius. In the southern hemisphere it is ascending from Gemini to Sagittarius and descending from Sagittarius to Gemini.

When the Moon is ascending, plant sap rises more strongly. The upper part of the plant fills with sap and vitality. This is a good time for cutting scions (for grafting). Fruit harvested during this period remains fresh for longer when stored.

When the Moon is descending, plants take root readily and connect well with their new location. This period is referred to as the **Transplanting Time.** Moving plants from one location to another is called *transplanting*. This is the case when young plants are moved from the seed bed into their final growing position but also when the gardener wishes to strengthen the root development of young fruit trees, shrubs or pot plants by frequently re-potting them. Sap movement is slower during the descending Moon. This is why it is a good time for trimming hedges, pruning trees and felling timber as well as applying compost to meadows, pastures and orchards.

Note that sowing is the moment when a seed is put into the soil; either the ascending or descending period can be used. It then needs time to germinate and grow. This is different from *transplanting*, which is best done during the descending Moon. These times are given in the calendar. **Northern Transplanting Times** refer to the northern hemisphere, and **Southern Transplanting Times** refer to the southern hemisphere. All other constellations and planetary aspects are equally valid in both hemispheres.

Local times

Times given are *Greenwich Mean Time* (GMT), using 24-hour clock with ^{h} after the time. Thus 15^h is 3 pm. *No account is taken of daylight saving (summer) time (DST).* Note 0^h is midnight at the beginning of a date, and 24^h is midnight at the end of the date.

Add (+) or subtract (−) times as below. For countries not listed check local time against GMT.

Europe

Britain, Ireland, Portugal: GMT
(March 25 to Oct 27, $+1^h$ for DST)
Iceland: GMT (no DST)
Central Europe: $+1^h$
(March 25 to Oct 27, $+2^h$ for DST)
Eastern Europe (Finland, etc.): $+2^h$
(March 25 to Oct 27, $+3^h$ for DST)
Russia (Moscow), Georgia: $+4^h$ (no DST)

Africa/Asia

Namibia: $+1^h$ (to March 31 & from Sep 2, $+2^h$ for DST)
South Africa: $+2^h$ (no DST)
Kenya: add 3^h (no DST)
Egypt: add 2^h (no DST)
Israel: add 2^h (March 23 to Oct 27, $+3^h$ for DST)
India: add $5\frac{1}{2}^h$ (no DST)
Philippines, China: add 8^h (no DST)
Japan, Korea: add 9^h (no DST)

Australia/New Zealand

Western Australia: $+8^h$ (no DST)
Northern Territory: $+9\frac{1}{2}^h$ (no DST)
South Australia: $+9\frac{1}{2}^h$ (to March 31 & from Oct 7, $+10\frac{1}{2}^h$ for DST)
Queensland: $+10^h$ (no DST)
ACT, NSW, Victoria, Tasmania: $+10^h$ (to March 31 & from Oct 7, $+11^h$ for DST)
New Zealand: $+12^h$ (to to March 31 & and from Sep 30, $+13^h$ for DST)

North America

Newfoundland Standard Time: $-3\frac{1}{2}^h$ (March 11 to Nov 3, $-2\frac{1}{2}^h$ for DST)
Atlantic Standard Time: -4^h (March 11 to Nov 3, -3^h for DST)
Eastern Standard Time: -5^h (March 11 to Nov 3, -4^h for DST)
Central Standard Time: -6^h (except Saskatchewan March 11 to Nov 3, -5^h for DST)
Mountain Standard Time: -7^h (except AZ, March 11 to Nov 3, -6^h for DST)
Pacific Standard Time: -8^h (March 11 to Nov 3, -7^h for DST)
Alaska Standard Time: -9^h (March 11 to Nov 3, -8^h for DST)
Hawaii Standard Time: -10^h (no DST)
Mexico (mostly CST): -6^h (April 1 to Oct 27, -5^h for DST)

South America

Argentina: -3^h (no DST)
Brazil (Eastern): -3^h (DST to Feb 17 and from Oct 21, -2^h)
Chile: -4^h (DST to May 12 and from Aug 12, -3^h)
Columbia, Peru: -5^h (no DST)

January 2018

All times in GMT

Date	Const. of Moon	Solar & lunar aspects	Trines	Moon El'ment	Parts of the plant enhanced by Moon or planets 0 1 2 3 4 5 6 7 8 9 10 11 12 13 14 15 16 17 18 19 20 21 22 23 24	Weather
1 Mon	♊ 8ʰ	☉-♐ **Pg** 22ʰ ⌒24ʰ		E/L	Root to 7ʰ 8-10ʰ	
2 Tue	♊	○ 2ʰ		L	Flower from 10ʰ	
3 Wed	♋ 4ʰ			L/W	Fl -3ʰ Leaf from 4ʰ	
4 Thu	♌ 14ʰ	☍ 8ʰ		W/H	Leaf to 4ʰ Fruit from 14ʰ	
5 Fri	♌			H	Fruit	St
6 Sat	♌			H	Fruit to 11ʰ Leaf from 12ʰ	St
7 Sun	♍ 1ʰ		▲	E	Lf - 3ʰ Root from 4ʰ	
8 Mon	♍	☾ 22ʰ		E	Root	
9 Tue	♍			E	Root	
10 Wed	♎ 15ʰ			E/L	Root to 14ʰ Flower from 15ʰ	
11 Thu	♎			L	Flower	Tr
12 Fri	♏ 3ʰ			L/W	-2ʰ Leaf from 3ʰ	
13 Sat	♏			W	Leaf	♄
14 Sun	♐ 17ʰ			W/H	-2ʰ	♄ St
15 Mon	♐	**Ag** 2ʰ ☋ 17ʰ ☿☊		H	Fruit from 16ʰ	Eq
16 Tue	♐			H	Fruit	
17 Wed	♑ 6ʰ	● 2ʰ		H/E	Fruit to 5ʰ Root from 6ʰ	Eq
18 Thu	♑	☉-♑ ☊ 14ʰ		E	Root to 10ʰ Root 19ʰ	St
19 Fri	♒ 14ʰ			E/L	Root to 13ʰ Flower from 14ʰ	Tr
20 Sat	♒			L	Flower	
21 Sun	♓ 15ʰ			L/W	Flower to 14ʰ Leaf from 15ʰ	
22 Mon	♓			W	Leaf	Tr
23 Tue	♓			W	Leaf	St Eq
24 Wed	♈ 13ʰ	☽ 22ʰ		W/H	Leaf to 12ʰ Fruit from 13ʰ	
25 Thu	♈			H	Fruit	
26 Fri	♉ 7ʰ			H/E	Fruit to 6ʰ Root from 7ʰ	St Eq
27 Sat	♉			E	Root	♄
28 Sun	♊ 19ʰ			E/L	Root to 18ʰ Flower 19ʰ	♄ Tr
29 Mon	♊	⌒ 12ʰ		L	Flower to 22ʰ	
30 Tue	♋ 15ʰ	**Pg** 10ʰ		L/W	23	St Eq
31 Wed	♋	☉•°○13ʰ ☍19ʰ		W	Leaf to 11ʰ	

Northern Transplanting Time (1–14)
Southern Transplanting Time (14–27)
NTT (28–31)

Mercury ☿	Venus ♀	Mars ♂	Jupiter ♃	Saturn ♄	Uranus ♅	Neptune ♆	Pluto ♇
♏ 10 ♐	♐	♎	♎	♐	♓	♒	♐
30 ♑	17 ♑	22 ♏			(R 2 D)		

NB: All zodiac symbols refer to astronomical constellations, not astrological signs (see p. 26)

Planetary aspects

(**Bold** = *visible to naked eye*)

1 ☽☍♄ 10ʰ ☽☍♀ 23ʰ
2 **☾☌♇ 14ʰ**
3
4
5
6 **☾☌♆ 5ʰ**

7 ☿△♁ 0ʰ ♂☌♃ 1ʰ
8
9 ☉☌♀ 8ʰ ♀☌♇ 9ʰ ☉☌♇ 9ʰ **☾☍♁ 10ʰ**
10
11 **☾☌♃ 8ʰ ☾☌♂ 13ʰ**
12
13 ☿☌♄ 7ʰ

14
15 **☾☌♄ 2ʰ** ☿☍♁ 3ʰ **☾☌☿ 7ʰ**
16 **☾☌♇ 11ʰ**
17 ☽☌♀ 7ʰ
18
19
20 ☽☌♆ 21ʰ

21
22
23
24 ☽☌♁ 4ʰ ☿☌♇ 21ʰ
25
26 ☽☍♃ 2ʰ ☽☍♂ 18ʰ
27

28
29 ☽☍♄ 2ʰ
30 ☽☍♇ 3ʰ ☽☍☿ 17ʰ
31 **☾☌♀ 23ʰ**

Planet (naked eye) visibility
Evening:
All night:
Morning: Mercury (to 19th), Mars, Jupiter, Saturn (from 14th)

January 2018

There are no clear weather indications at the beginning of the year. On Jan 10 Mercury joins Venus in Sagittarius and brings Warmth adding to the Light influences coming from Mars, Jupiter and Neptune. Colder days can only be expected around the middle of the month.

Northern Transplanting Time
Jan 2 2ʰ to Jan 15 15ʰ and
Jan 29 14ʰ to Feb 11
Southern Transplanting Time
Dec 19 to Jan 1 22ʰ and
Jan 15 19ʰ to Jan 29 10ʰ

The transplanting time is a good time for **pruning fruit trees, vines and hedges.** Fruit and Flower times are preferred for this work. Avoid unfavourable times.

When **milk processing** it is best to avoid unfavourable times. This applies to both butter and cheese making. Milk which has been produced at Warmth/Fruit times yields the highest butterfat content. This is also the case on days with a tendency for thunderstorms. Times of moon perigee (**Pg**) are almost always unfavourable for milk processing and even yoghurt will not turn out well. Starter cultures from such days decay rapidly and it is advisable to produce double the amount the day before. Milk loves Light and Warmth times best of all. Water times are unsuitable.

Southern hemisphere harvest time for seeds
Fruit seeds: Jan 4 14ʰ to Jan 6 11ʰ and at other Fruit times, always avoiding unfavourable times.
Flower seeds: Flower times.
Leaf seeds: Leaf times.
Root seeds: Root times.

Control slugs from Jan 3 4ʰ to Jan 4 13ʰ.

Biodynamic preparations: This year there are no positive aspects for making biodynamic preparations, except for chamomile in Aug/Sep.

Unfavourable time 33

All times in GMT

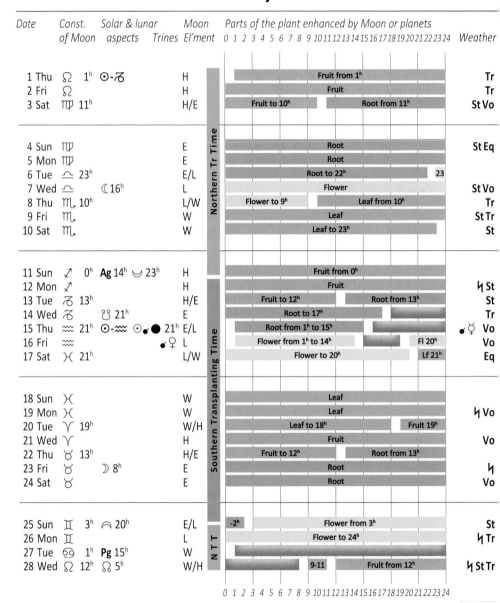

Date	Const. of Moon	Solar & lunar aspects	Trines	Moon El'ment	Parts of the plant enhanced by Moon or planets	Weather
1 Thu	♌ 1ʰ	☉-♑		H	Fruit from 1ʰ	Tr
2 Fri	♌			H	Fruit	Tr
3 Sat	♍ 11ʰ			H/E	Fruit to 10ʰ / Root from 11ʰ	St Vo
4 Sun	♍			E	Root	St Eq
5 Mon	♍			E	Root	
6 Tue	♎ 23ʰ			E/L	Root to 22ʰ / 23	
7 Wed	♎	☾ 16ʰ		L	Flower	St Vo
8 Thu	♏ 10ʰ			L/W	Flower to 9ʰ / Leaf from 10ʰ	Tr
9 Fri	♏			W	Leaf	St Tr
10 Sat	♏			W	Leaf to 23ʰ	St
11 Sun	♐ 0ʰ	**Ag** 14ʰ ☋ 23ʰ		H	Fruit from 0ʰ	
12 Mon	♐			H	Fruit	♄ St
13 Tue	♑ 13ʰ			H/E	Fruit to 12ʰ / Root from 13ʰ	St
14 Wed	♑	☍ 21ʰ		E	Root to 17ʰ	Tr
15 Thu	♒ 21ʰ	☉-♒ ☉● 21ʰ		E/L	Root from 1ʰ to 15ʰ	☌☿ Vo
16 Fri	♒	☌♀		L	Flower from 1ʰ to 14ʰ / Fl 20ʰ	Vo
17 Sat	♓ 21ʰ			L/W	Flower to 20ʰ / Lf 21ʰ	Eq
18 Sun	♓			W	Leaf	
19 Mon	♓			W	Leaf	♄ Vo
20 Tue	♈ 19ʰ			W/H	Leaf to 18ʰ / Fruit 19ʰ	
21 Wed	♈			H	Fruit	Vo
22 Thu	♉ 13ʰ			H/E	Fruit to 12ʰ / Root from 13ʰ	
23 Fri	♉	☽ 8ʰ		E	Root	♄
24 Sat	♉			E	Root	Vo
25 Sun	♊ 3ʰ	⚹ 20ʰ		E/L	-2ʰ / Flower from 3ʰ	St
26 Mon	♊			L	Flower to 24ʰ	♄ Tr
27 Tue	♋ 1ʰ	**Pg** 15ʰ		W		♄
28 Wed	♌ 12ʰ	☍ 5ʰ		W/H	9-11 / Fruit from 12ʰ	♄ St Tr

Northern Tr Time (4 Sun – 10 Sat)
Southern Transplanting Time (11 Sun – 24 Sat)
NTT (25 Sun – 28 Wed)

0 1 2 3 4 5 6 7 8 9 10 11 12 13 14 15 16 17 18 19 20 21 22 23 24

Mercury ☿	Venus ♀	Mars ♂	Jupiter ♃	Saturn ♄	Uranus ♅	Neptune ♆	Pluto ♇
♑	♓ 8 ♒	♏	♎	♐	♓	♒	♐
16 ♒	28 ♓						

NB: All zodiac symbols refer to astronomical constellations, not astrological signs (see p. 26,

Planetary aspects
(Bold = *visible to naked eye*)

February 2018

1	
2	☽ ☌ ♆ 17ʰ
3	
4	
5	☽ ☌ ⊕ 19ʰ
6	
7	**☽ ☌ ♃ 22ʰ**
8	
9	**☽ ☌ ♂ 7ʰ**
10	
11	**☽ ☌ ♄ 14ʰ**
12	☽ ☌ ♇ 19ʰ
13	
14	
15	☽ • ☿ 18ʰ
16	☽ • ♀ 17ʰ
17	☽ ☌ ♆ 5ʰ ☉ ☌ ☿ 13ʰ
18	
19	
20	☽ ☌ ⊕ 11ʰ
21	♀ ☌ ♆ 19ʰ
22	☽ ☍ ♃ 12ʰ
23	
24	☽ ☍ ♂ 6ʰ
25	☿ ☌ ♆ 13ʰ ☽ ☍ ♄ 15ʰ
26	☽ ☍ ♇ 13ʰ
27	
28	

We can expect winter to finally arrive in the first two weeks, but from the middle of the month it is likely to turn mild again thanks to the Light and Warmth aspects that prevent extended periods of stable temperatures developing.

Northern Transplanting Time
Jan 29 to Feb 11 22ʰ and
Feb 25 22ʰ to March 11
Southern Transplanting Time
Feb 12 2ʰ to Feb 25 18ʰ

Vines, fruit trees and shrubs can be pruned during Transplanting Time selecting Flower and Fruit times in preference. Avoid unfavourable times.

Best times for taking **willow cuttings for hedges and fences:** At Flower times outside Transplanting Time. In warm areas at Flower times during Transplanting Time to avoid too strong a sap current.

Southern hemisphere harvest time for seeds
Fruit seeds: Feb 1 1ʰ to Feb 3 10ʰ, and Feb 11 0ʰ to Feb 13 12ʰ and at other Fruit times.
Flower seeds: Feb 16 1ʰ to Feb 17 20ʰ, avoiding unfavourable times, and at other Flower times.

Control slugs from Feb 28 9ʰ to 11ʰ.

Planet (naked eye) visibility
Evening: Venus (from 10th)
All night:
Morning: Mars, Jupiter, Saturn

Unfavourable time   35

March 2018

Date	Const. of Moon	Solar & lunar aspects	Trines	Moon El'ment	Parts of the plant enhanced by Moon or planets	Weather

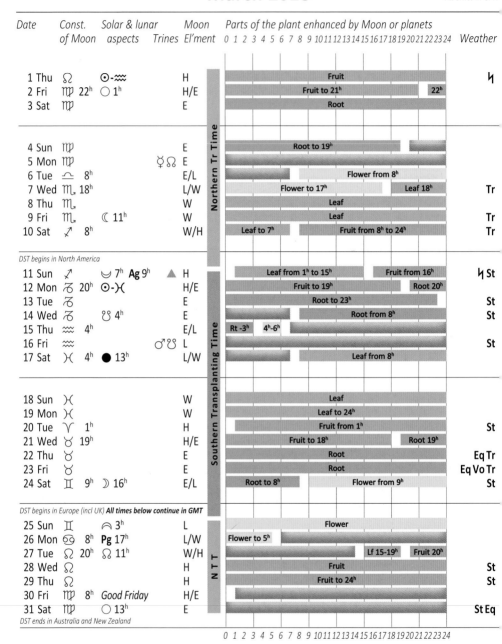

1 Thu ♌ ☉-♒ H — Fruit — ♄
2 Fri ♍ 22ʰ ○ 1ʰ H/E — Fruit to 21ʰ / 22ʰ
3 Sat ♍ E — Root

4 Sun ♍ E — Root to 19ʰ
5 Mon ♍ ☿♌ E
6 Tue ♎ 8ʰ E/L — Flower from 8ʰ
7 Wed ♏ 18ʰ L/W — Flower to 17ʰ / Leaf 18ʰ — Tr
8 Thu ♏ W — Leaf
9 Fri ♏ ☾ 11ʰ W — Leaf — Tr
10 Sat ♐ 8ʰ W/H — Leaf to 7ʰ / Fruit from 8ʰ to 24ʰ — Tr

DST begins in North America

Northern Tr Time

11 Sun ♐ ♉ 7ʰ **Ag 9ʰ** ▲ H — Leaf from 1ʰ to 15ʰ / Fruit from 16ʰ — ♄ St
12 Mon ♑ 20ʰ ☉-♓ H/E — Fruit to 19ʰ / Root 20ʰ
13 Tue ♑ E — Root to 23ʰ — St
14 Wed ♑ ☊ 4ʰ E — Root from 8ʰ — St
15 Thu ♒ 4ʰ E/L — Rt -3ʰ / 4ʰ-6ʰ
16 Fri ♒ ♂☊ L — St
17 Sat ♓ 4ʰ ● 13ʰ L/W — Leaf from 8ʰ

18 Sun ♓ W — Leaf
19 Mon ♓ W — Leaf to 24ʰ
20 Tue ♈ 1ʰ H — Fruit from 1ʰ — St
21 Wed ♉ 19ʰ H/E — Fruit to 18ʰ / Root 19ʰ
22 Thu ♉ E — Root — Eq Tr
23 Fri ♉ E — Root — Eq Vo Tr
24 Sat ♊ 9ʰ ☽ 16ʰ E/L — Root to 8ʰ / Flower from 9ʰ — St

Southern Transplanting Time

DST begins in Europe (incl UK) **All times below continue in GMT**

25 Sun ♊ ⌒ 3ʰ L — Flower
26 Mon ♋ 8ʰ **Pg 17ʰ** L/W — Flower to 5ʰ
27 Tue ♌ 20ʰ ♌ 11ʰ W/H — Lf 15-19ʰ / Fruit 20ʰ
28 Wed ♌ H — Fruit — St
29 Thu ♌ H — Fruit to 24ʰ — St
30 Fri ♍ 8ʰ *Good Friday* H/E
31 Sat ♍ ○ 13ʰ E — St Eq

N T T

DST ends in Australia and New Zealand

Mercury ☿	Venus ♀	Mars ♂	Jupiter ♃	Saturn ♄	Uranus ♅	Neptune ♆	Pluto ♇
♒ 1 ♓	♓	♏	♎	♐	♓	♒	♐
(23 R)	30 ♈	15 ♐	(9 R)				

NB: All zodiac symbols refer to astronomical constellations, not astrological signs (see p. 26)

Planetary aspects
(**Bold** = *visible to naked eye*)

1	$♀△♃$ 11^h
2	$☾♂°♅$ 5^h $☿△♃$ 13^h $☾♂°☿$ 22^h
3	$☾♂°♀$ 0^h
4	$☉♂♅$ 14^h $☿♂♀$ 18^h
5	$☾♂°⚸$ 6^h $☿♌$ 19^h
6	
7	$☾♂♃$ 9^h
8	
9	
10	$☾♂♂$ 1^h
11	$☾♂♄$ 2^h $♂△⚸$ 11^h
12	$☾♂♇$ 4^h
13	
14	
15	
16	$☾♂♅$ 15^h $♂°♌$ 19^h
17	
18	$☽♂♀$ 23^h
19	$☽♂☿$ 0^h $☽♂⚸$ 20^h
20	$☿♂♀$ 4^h
21	$☽♂♃$ 17^h
22	
23	
24	$☽♂°♂$ 17^h
25	$☽♂°♄$ 5^h $☽♂°♇$ 21^h
26	
27	
28	
29	$♀♂⚸$ 1^h $☽♂°♅$ 16^h
30	
31	$☾♂°☿$ 16^h

March 2018

Mars and Uranus, together with Mercury and Venus, are in positions that will ensure adequate spring rain. Jupiter will bring the Light and Saturn the Warmth needed for a good start to growth.

Northern Transplanting Time
Feb 25 to March 11 5^h and
March 25 5^h to April 7
Southern Transplanting Time
March 11 9^h to March 25 1^h

Willow cuttings for **pollen production** are best cut from March 6 8^h to March 7 17^h; and for **honey flow** from March 27 20^h to end of March 29. Avoid unfavourable times.

Cuttings for grafting: Cut outside Transplanting Time during ascending Moon – always choosing times (Fruit, Leaf, etc.) according to the part of plant to be enhanced.

Control slugs from March 27 15^h to 19^h.

Southern hemisphere harvest time for seeds
Fruit seeds: March 27 20^h to end of March 29, and at other Fruit times.
Flower seeds: March 6 8^h to March 7 17^h and at other Flower times.
Leaf seeds: Leaf times.
Root seeds: Root times.
    Always avoid unfavourable times.

Biodynamic preparations: Pick dandelion in March or April in the mornings during Flower times. The flowers should not be quite open in the centre. Dry them on paper in the shade, not in bright sunlight.

Planet (naked eye) visibility
Evening: Mercury (2nd to 26th), Venus
All night:
Morning: Mars, Jupiter, Saturn

Unfavourable time

April 2018

Date	Const. of Moon	Solar & lunar aspects	Trines	Moon El'ment	Parts of the plant enhanced by Moon or planets	Weather

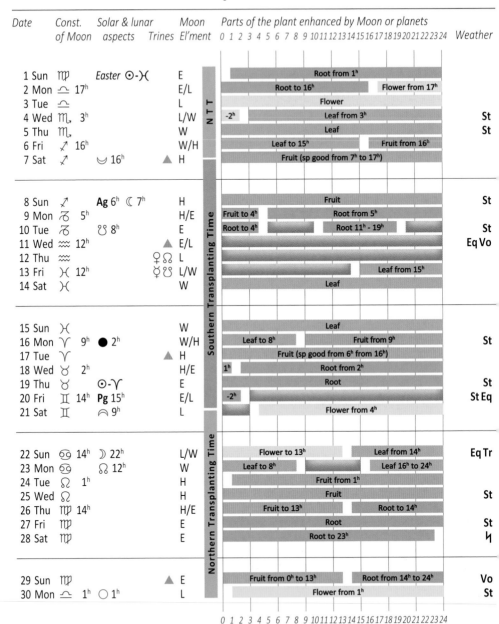

Date	Const. of Moon	Solar & lunar aspects	Trines	Moon El'ment	0 1 2 3 4 5 6 7 8 9 10 11 12 13 14 15 16 17 18 19 20 21 22 23 24	Weather
1 Sun	♍	Easter ☉-♓		E	Root from 1ʰ	
2 Mon	♎ 17ʰ			E/L	Root to 16ʰ — Flower from 17ʰ	
3 Tue	♎			L	Flower	
4 Wed	♏ 3ʰ			L/W	-2ʰ — Leaf from 3ʰ	St
5 Thu	♏			W	Leaf	St
6 Fri	♐ 16ʰ			W/H	Leaf to 15ʰ — Fruit from 16ʰ	
7 Sat	♐	☋ 16ʰ	▲	H	Fruit (sp good from 7ʰ to 17ʰ)	
8 Sun	♐	Ag 6ʰ ☾ 7ʰ		H	Fruit	St
9 Mon	♑ 5ʰ			H/E	Fruit to 4ʰ — Root from 5ʰ	
10 Tue	♑	☊ 8ʰ		E	Root to 4ʰ — Root 11ʰ - 19ʰ	St
11 Wed	♒ 12ʰ		▲	E/L		Eq Vo
12 Thu	♒		♀☍	L		
13 Fri	♓ 12ʰ		☿☍	L/W	Leaf from 15ʰ	
14 Sat	♓			W	Leaf	
15 Sun	♓			W	Leaf	
16 Mon	♈ 9ʰ	● 2ʰ		W/H	Leaf to 8ʰ — Fruit from 9ʰ	St
17 Tue	♈		▲	H	Fruit (sp good from 6ʰ from 16ʰ)	
18 Wed	♉ 2ʰ			H/E	1ʰ — Root from 2ʰ	
19 Thu	♉	☉-♈		E	Root	St
20 Fri	♊ 14ʰ	Pg 15ʰ		E/L	-2ʰ	St Eq
21 Sat	♊	☌ 9ʰ		L	Flower from 4ʰ	
22 Sun	♋ 14ʰ	☽ 22ʰ		L/W	Flower to 13ʰ — Leaf from 14ʰ	Eq Tr
23 Mon	♋	☋ 12ʰ		W	Leaf to 8ʰ — Leaf 16ʰ to 24ʰ	
24 Tue	♌ 1ʰ			H	Fruit from 1ʰ	
25 Wed	♌			H	Fruit	St
26 Thu	♍ 14ʰ			H/E	Fruit to 13ʰ — Root from 14ʰ	
27 Fri	♍			E	Root	St
28 Sat	♍			E	Root to 23ʰ	♄
29 Sun	♍		▲	E	Fruit from 0ʰ to 13ʰ — Root from 14ʰ to 24ʰ	Vo
30 Mon	♎ 1ʰ	○ 1ʰ		L	Flower from 1ʰ	St

0 1 2 3 4 5 6 7 8 9 10 11 12 13 14 15 16 17 18 19 20 21 22 23 24

(Vertical labels between sections: NTT; Southern Transplanting Time; Northern Transplanting Time)

Mercury ☿	Venus ♀	Mars ♂	Jupiter ♃	Saturn ♄	Uranus ♅	Neptune ♆	Pluto ♇
♓	♈	♐	♎	♐	♓	♒	♐
(R 15 D)	19 ♉		(R)	(18 R)			(22 R)

NB: All zodiac symbols refer to astronomical constellations, not astrological signs (see p. 26)

Planetary aspects

(**Bold** = *visible to naked eye*)

1 ☉☌☿ 18h ☾☍⛢ 19h
2 ☾☍♀ 3h **♂☌♄ 16h**
3 **☾☌♃ 16h**
4
5
6
7 **☾☌♄ 12h** ♀△♄ 14h **☾☌♂ 18h**

8 ☾☌♇ 13h
9
10
11 ♀△♂ 6h
12 ♀☊ 4h
13 ☾☌♆ 0h ☿☋ 2h
14 ☾☌☿ 12h

15
16 ☽☌⛢ 6h
17 ♀☍♃ 7h ♀△♇ 13h ☽☍♃ 21h **☽☌♀ 22h**
18 ☉☌⛢ 14h
19
20
21 ☽☍♄ 6h ☽☍♂ 23h

22 ☽☍♇ 2h
23
24
25
26 ☽☍♆ 0h ♂☌♇ 11h
27 ☽☍☿ 20h
28

29 ☽☍⛢ 6h ☉△♄ 10h
30 **☾☌♃ 19h**

Planet (naked eye) visibility
Evening: Venus
All night: Jupiter
Morning: Mars, Saturn

April 2018

The planetary aspects of this month suggest that April will not live up to its reputation. With three planets in Warmth constellations, two in Light constellations and three Warmth trines, Mercury will not be able to bring much moisture.

Northern Transplanting Time
March 25 to April 7 14h and
April 21 11h to May 4
Southern Transplanting Time
April 7 18h to April 21 7h

Grafting of fruiting shrubs at Fruit times outside transplanting times.

Grafting of flowering shrubs at Flower times outside transplanting times.

Control
Slugs from April 22 14h to April 23 24h.
Clothes and wax moths from April 13 15h to April 16 8h.

Southern hemisphere harvest time for seeds
Fruit seeds: Specially good April 7 from 7h to 17h and April 24 1h to April 26 13h, and at other Fruit times.
Flower seeds April 2 17h to April 4 2h and other at Flower times.
Leaf seeds at Leaf times, and **Root seeds** at Root times. Always avoid unfavourable times.

Unfavourable time

May 2018

Date	Const. of Moon	Solar & lunar aspects	Moon Trines El'ment	Parts of the plant enhanced by Moon or planets	Weather

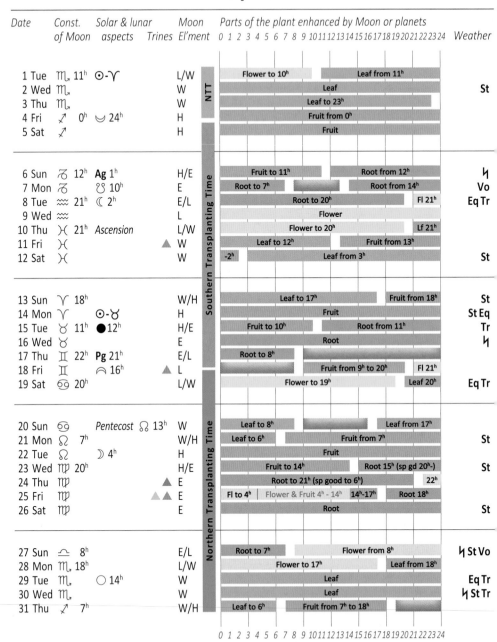

Date	Const. of Moon	Solar & lunar aspects	Trines El'ment	Weather
1 Tue	♏ 11ʰ ☉-♈		L/W	St
2 Wed	♏		W	
3 Thu	♏		W	
4 Fri	♐ 0ʰ ☌ 24ʰ		H	
5 Sat	♐		H	
6 Sun	♑ 12ʰ **Ag** 1ʰ		H/E	♄
7 Mon	♑ ☍ 10ʰ		E	Vo
8 Tue	♒ 21ʰ ☽ 2ʰ		E/L	Eq Tr
9 Wed	♒		L	
10 Thu	♓ 21ʰ Ascension		L/W	
11 Fri	♓		W	
12 Sat	♓		W	St
13 Sun	♈ 18ʰ		W/H	St
14 Mon	♈ ☉-♉		H	St Eq
15 Tue	♉ 11ʰ ● 12ʰ		H/E	Tr
16 Wed	♉		E	♄
17 Thu	♊ 22ʰ **Pg** 21ʰ		E/L	
18 Fri	♊ ☌ 16ʰ		L	
19 Sat	♋ 20ʰ		L/W	Eq Tr
20 Sun	♋ Pentecost ☍ 13ʰ		W	
21 Mon	♌ 7ʰ		W/H	St
22 Tue	♌ ☽ 4ʰ		H	
23 Wed	♍ 20ʰ		H/E	St
24 Thu	♍		E	
25 Fri	♍		E	
26 Sat	♍		E	St
27 Sun	♎ 8ʰ		E/L	♄ St Vo
28 Mon	♏ 18ʰ		L/W	
29 Tue	♏ ○ 14ʰ		W	Eq Tr
30 Wed	♏		W	♄ St Tr
31 Thu	♐ 7ʰ		W/H	

NTT

Southern Transplanting Time

Northern Transplanting Time

0 1 2 3 4 5 6 7 8 9 10 11 12 13 14 15 16 17 18 19 20 21 22 23 24

Mercury ☿	Venus ♀	Mars ♂	Jupiter ♃	Saturn ♄	Uranus ♅	Neptune ♆	Pluto ♇
♓ 13 ♈	♉	♐	♎	♐	♓	♒	♐
26 ♉	19 ♊	12 ♑	(R)	(R)	9 ♈		(R)

NB: All zodiac symbols refer to astronomical constellations, not astrological signs (see p. 26)

Planetary aspects
(**Bold** = *visible to naked eye)*

1
2 ☾☍♀ 9^h
3
4 **☾☌♄ 20^h**
5 ☾☌♇ 21^h
6 **☾☌♂ 6^h**
7
8
9 ☉☍♃ 2^h
10 ☾☌♆ 10^h
11 ☉△♇ 23^h
12
13 ☿☌♅ 11^h ☾☌♅ 18^h ☾☌☿ 19^h
14
15 ☾☍♃ 0^h
16
17 **☽☌♀ 18^h** ☽☌♀ 18^h
18 ☽☍♄ 12^h ☿△♄ 17^h
19 ☽☍♇ 8^h
20 ☽☍♂ 2^h
21
22
23 ☿☍♃ 6^h ☽☍♆ 7^h
24 ☉△♂ 3^h
25 ♃△♆ 9^h ☿△♇ 14^h
26 ♀☍♄ 7^h ☽☍♅ 15^h
27 **☽☌♃ 20^h**
28 ☽☍☿ 17^h
29
30
31

Planet (naked eye) visibility
Evening: Venus
All night: Jupiter, Saturn
Morning: Mars

May 2018

There is likely to be a great deal of diversity in May. Cool nights brought by Venus will be reinforced later on by Mars. This probably means having to contend with more aphids, and that will please no one apart from beekeepers.

Jupiter and later on Venus and some Fruit and Flower trines will encourage good cereal growth. The late warming up of the soil however could mean growth during the first half of the month is slow. The three Warmth–Light oppositions (on May 9, 23 and 26) are more likely to raise our spirits than stimulate plant growth.

Northern Transplanting Time
April 21 to May 4 22^h and
May 18 18^h to June 1
Southern Transplanting Time
May 5 2^h to May 18 14^h

The **soil warms up** on May 14.

Transplant **table potatoes** at Root times.
Transplant **seed potatoes** for 2019 from May 13 18^h to May 15 10^h.

Hay should be cut between May 18 9^h and May 19 19^h, and at other Flower times.

Control:
Moths from May 10 21^h to May 13 17^h.
Flies by burning fly papers in the cow barn at Flower times.
Chitinous insects, wheat weevil, Colorado beetle and varroa from May 15 11^h to May 17 8^h.
Mole crickets ash from May 28 18^h to May 31 6^h.

Begin **queen bee** rearing (grafting or larval transfer, comb insertion, cell punching) between May 18 9^h and May 19 19^h and at other Flower times.

Biodynamic preparations: The preparations can be taken out of the ground after May 14, avoiding unfavourable times.

Unfavourable time

All times in GMT

Date	Const. of Moon	Solar & lunar aspects	Trines	Moon El'ment	Parts of the plant enhanced by Moon or planets	Weather

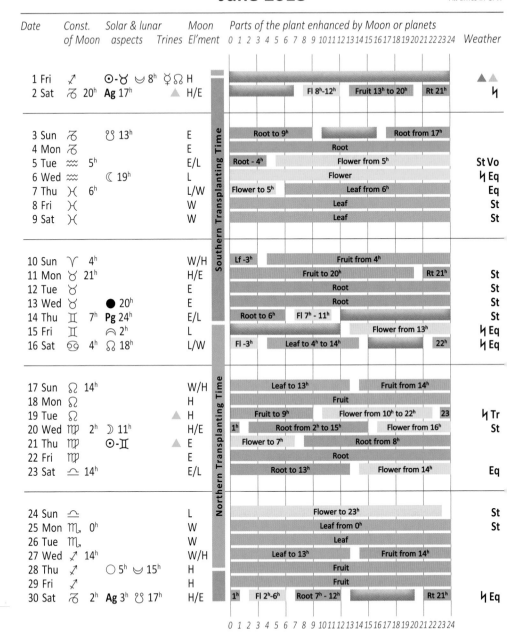

1 Fri ♐	☉-♉ ☾ 8ʰ ☿♌ H				▲ ▲
2 Sat ♑ 20ʰ **Ag 17ʰ**	▲ H/E	Fl 8ʰ-12ʰ Fruit 13ʰ to 20ʰ Rt 21ʰ			♄

Southern Transplanting Time

3 Sun ♑	♉ 13ʰ E	Root to 9ʰ Root from 17ʰ			
4 Mon ♑	E	Root			
5 Tue ♒ 5ʰ	E/L	Root - 4ʰ Flower from 5ʰ			St Vo
6 Wed ♒	☽ 19ʰ L	Flower			♄ Eq
7 Thu ♓ 6ʰ	L/W	Flower to 5ʰ Leaf from 6ʰ			Eq
8 Fri ♓	W	Leaf			St
9 Sat ♓	W	Leaf			St

10 Sun ♈ 4ʰ	W/H	Lf -3ʰ Fruit from 4ʰ			St
11 Mon ♉ 21ʰ	H/E	Fruit to 20ʰ Rt 21ʰ			St
12 Tue ♉	E	Root			St
13 Wed ♉ ● 20ʰ	E	Root			St
14 Thu ♊ 7ʰ **Pg 24ʰ**	E/L	Root to 6ʰ Fl 7ʰ - 11ʰ			St
15 Fri ♊ ⌒ 2ʰ	L	Flower from 13ʰ			♄ Eq
16 Sat ♋ 4ʰ ♌ 18ʰ	L/W	Fl -3ʰ Leaf to 4ʰ to 14ʰ 22ʰ			♄ Eq

Northern Transplanting Time

17 Sun ♌ 14ʰ	W/H	Leaf to 13ʰ Fruit from 14ʰ			
18 Mon ♌	H	Fruit			
19 Tue ♌	▲ H	Fruit to 9ʰ Flower from 10ʰ to 22ʰ 23			♄ Tr
20 Wed ♍ 2ʰ ☽ 11ʰ	H/E	1ʰ Root from 2ʰ to 15ʰ Flower from 16ʰ			St
21 Thu ♍ ☉-♊	▲ E	Flower to 7ʰ Root from 8ʰ			
22 Fri ♍	E	Root			
23 Sat ♎ 14ʰ	E/L	Root to 13ʰ Flower from 14ʰ			Eq

24 Sun ♎	L	Flower to 23ʰ			St
25 Mon ♏ 0ʰ	W	Leaf from 0ʰ			St
26 Tue ♏	W	Leaf			
27 Wed ♐ 14ʰ	W/H	Leaf to 13ʰ Fruit from 14ʰ			
28 Thu ♐ ○ 5ʰ ☾ 15ʰ	H	Fruit			
29 Fri ♐	H	Fruit			
30 Sat ♑ 2ʰ **Ag 3ʰ** ♌ 17ʰ	H/E	1ʰ Fl 2ʰ-6ʰ Root 7ʰ - 12ʰ Rt 21ʰ			♄ Eq

0 1 2 3 4 5 6 7 8 9 10 11 12 13 14 15 16 17 18 19 20 21 22 23 24

Mercury ☿	Venus ♀	Mars ♂	Jupiter ♃	Saturn ♄	Uranus ♅	Neptune ♆	Pluto ♇
♉ 12 ♊	♊ 11 ♋	♑	♎	♐	♈	♒	♐
27 ♋	30 ♌	(26 R)	(R)	(R)		(18 R)	(R)

NB: All zodiac symbols refer to astronomical constellations, not astrological signs (see p. 26)

Planetary aspects
(**Bold** = *visible to naked eye)*

1 **☾☌♄ 1^h** ☿△♂ 14^h **♀△♃ 15^h** ☾☍♀ 17^h ☿☊ 18^h
2 ☾☌♇ 4^h ♀△♆ 9^h
3 **☾☌♂ 10^h**
4
5
6 ☉☌☿ 2^h ♀☍♇ 2^h ☾☌♆ 19^h
7
8
9
10 ☾☌♅ 6^h
11 ☾☍♃ 5^h
12
13
14 ☽☌☿ 13^h ☽☍♄ 18^h
15 ☽☍♇ 16^h
16 ☿☍♄ 2^h **☽☌♀ 12^h** ☽☍♂ 21^h
17
18
19 ☽☍♆ 13^h ☿△♃ 20^h
20
21 ☿△♆ 4^h ♀☍♂ 17^h
22 ☽☍♅ 22^h
23 ☿☍♇ 9^h **☽☌♃ 21^h**
24
25
26
27 ☉☍♄ 13^h
28 **☽☌♄ 4^h**
29 ☾☌♇ 9^h
30 ☾☍☿ 8^h **☾☌♂ 23^h**

Planet (naked eye) visibility
Evening: Venus
All night: Jupiter, Saturn
Morning: Mars

June 2018

The presence of Mercury and Mars in Earth constellations means that we need to reckon with a cool start to the month. Venus, Jupiter and later on Mercury and the four Light trines will however bring some light into the cool and moist conditions which Venus and Mercury will facilitate.

Northern Transplanting Time
May 18 to June 1 6^h and
June 15 4^h to June 28 13^h
Southern Transplanting Time
June 1 10^h to June 14 24^h and
June 28 17^h to July 12

Cut **hay** at Flower times.

Begin **queen bee** rearing at Fruit and Flower times, avoiding unfavourable times.

Control:
Flies by burning fly papers in the cow barn from June 23 14^h to June 24 23^h, and at other Flower times.
Grasshoppers from June 5 5^h to June 7 5^h.

Unfavourable time

July 2018

All times in GMT

Date	Const. of Moon	Solar & lunar aspects	Trines	Moon El'ment	Parts of the plant enhanced by Moon or planets	Weather

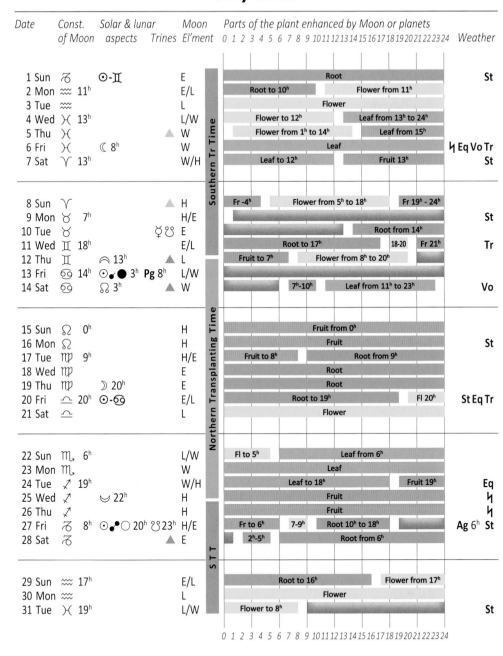

0 1 2 3 4 5 6 7 8 9 10 11 12 13 14 15 16 17 18 19 20 21 22 23 24

Southern Tr Time / Northern Transplanting Time / S T T

1 Sun ♑	☉-♊		E	Root	St
2 Mon ♒ 11ʰ			E/L	Root to 10ʰ / Flower from 11ʰ	
3 Tue ♒			L	Flower	
4 Wed ♓ 13ʰ			L/W	Flower to 12ʰ / Leaf from 13ʰ to 24ʰ	
5 Thu ♓		▲	W	Flower from 1ʰ to 14ʰ / Leaf from 15ʰ	
6 Fri ♓	☾ 8ʰ		W	Leaf	♄ Eq Vo Tr
7 Sat ♈ 13ʰ			W/H	Leaf to 12ʰ / Fruit 13ʰ	St
8 Sun ♈		▲	H	Fr -4ʰ / Flower from 5ʰ to 18ʰ / Fr 19ʰ - 24ʰ	
9 Mon ♉ 7ʰ			H/E		St
10 Tue ♉	☿☍		E	Root from 14ʰ	
11 Wed ♊ 18ʰ			E/L	Root to 17ʰ / 18-20 / Fr 21ʰ	Tr
12 Thu ♊	♐ 13ʰ	▲	L	Fruit to 7ʰ / Flower from 8ʰ to 20ʰ	
13 Fri ♋ 14ʰ	☉•● 3ʰ Pg 8ʰ		L/W		
14 Sat ♋	♌ 3ʰ	▲	W	7ʰ-10ʰ / Leaf from 11ʰ to 23ʰ	Vo
15 Sun ♌ 0ʰ			H	Fruit from 0ʰ	
16 Mon ♌			H	Fruit	St
17 Tue ♍ 9ʰ			H/E	Fruit to 8ʰ / Root from 9ʰ	
18 Wed ♍			E	Root	
19 Thu ♍	☽ 20ʰ		E	Root	
20 Fri ♎ 20ʰ	☉-♋		E/L	Root to 19ʰ / Fl 20ʰ	St Eq Tr
21 Sat ♎			L	Flower	
22 Sun ♏ 6ʰ			L/W	Fl to 5ʰ / Leaf from 6ʰ	
23 Mon ♏			W	Leaf	
24 Tue ♐ 19ʰ			W/H	Leaf to 18ʰ / Fruit 19ʰ	Eq
25 Wed ♐	� 22ʰ		H	Fruit	♄
26 Thu ♐			H	Fruit	♄
27 Fri ♑ 8ʰ	☉•○ 20ʰ ☍23ʰ		H/E	Fr to 6ʰ / 7-9ʰ / Root 10ʰ to 18ʰ	Ag 6ʰ St
28 Sat ♑		▲	E	2ʰ-5ʰ / Root from 6ʰ	
29 Sun ♒ 17ʰ			E/L	Root to 16ʰ / Flower from 17ʰ	
30 Mon ♒			L	Flower	
31 Tue ♓ 19ʰ			L/W	Flower to 8ʰ	St

0 1 2 3 4 5 6 7 8 9 10 11 12 13 14 15 16 17 18 19 20 21 22 23 24

Mercury ☿	Venus ♀	Mars ♂	Jupiter ♃	Saturn ♄	Uranus ♅	Neptune ♆	Pluto ♇
♋ 14 ♌	♌	♑	♎	♐	♈	♒	♐
(26 R)	31 ♍	(R)	(R 10 D)	(R)		(R)	(R)

NB: All zodiac symbols refer to astronomical constellations, not astrological signs (see p. 26)

44

Planetary aspects
(**Bold** = *visible to naked eye*)

1	☾ ☌ ☌ ♀ 23ʰ
2	
3	
4	☾ ☌ ♆ 2ʰ
5	☉ △ ♃ 11ʰ ☿ ☌ ☌ ♂ 12ʰ
6	
7	☾ ☌ ⊕ 17ʰ
8	☾ ☌ ☌ ♃ 13ʰ ☉ △ ♆ 15ʰ
9	
10	☿ ☍ 1ʰ
11	
12	☾ ☌ ♄ 2ʰ ♀ △ ⊕ 3ʰ ☉ ☌ ♇ 10ʰ
13	☾ ☌ ♇ 2ʰ
14	☽ ☌ ♂ 5ʰ ♀ △ ♄ 7ʰ ☽ ☌ ☿ 23ʰ
15	
16	☽ ☌ ♀ 5ʰ ☽ ☌ ♆ 20ʰ
17	
18	
19	
20	☽ ☌ ⊕ 6ʰ
21	☽ ☌ ♃ 2ʰ
22	
23	
24	♀ ☌ ♆ 20ʰ
25	☽ ☌ ♄ 6ʰ
26	☽ ☌ ♇ 14ʰ
27	☉ ☌ ♂ 5ʰ ☽ ☌ ♂ 19ʰ
28	♀ △ ♇ 1ʰ
29	☾ ☌ ☌ ☿ 9ʰ
30	
31	☾ ☌ ♆ 8ʰ ☾ ☌ ☌ ♀ 23ʰ

Planet (naked eye) visibility
Evening: **Venus**
All night: **Mars, Jupiter, Saturn**
Morning:

July 2018

Warmth constellations dominate the second half of the month and this could presage a good grain ripening period. It will also be good for rape crops. Three Warmth and two Light trines will almost certainly benefit the ripening processes.

Northern Transplanting Time
July 12 15ʰ to July 25 20ʰ
Southern Transplanting Time
June 28 to July 12 11ʰ
July 26 0ʰ to Aug 8

Late hay cut at Flower times.

Summer harvest for seeds:
Flower plants: Harvest at Flower times, specially in the first half of the month.
   Fruit plants from July 15 0ʰ to July 17 8ʰ, or at other Fruit times.
   Harvest **leaf plants** at Leaf times.
   Harvest **root plants** at Root times, especially July 10 14ʰ to July 11 17ʰ, and July 17 9ʰ to July 20 19ʰ.
   Always avoid unfavourable times.

Control
Flies: burn fly papers in the cow barn at Flower times.
Slugs: burn between July 14 11ʰ and 23ʰ. Spray leaf plants and the soil with horn silica early in the morning during Leaf times.
Grasshoppers from June 11 18ʰ to June 12 20ʰ.

Biodynamic preparations
Pick **Valerian** flowers at Flower times early in the morning while there is still plenty of night time moisture around. The juice should be pressed out immediately without adding any water or leaving the plants in water. Juice to which water has been added will not keep long. It is good to start looking for the places where valerian is growing in June, so that the harvest can proceed in an efficient way.

August 2018

Date	Const. of Moon	Solar & lunar aspects	Moon Trines	El'ment	Parts of the plant enhanced by Moon or planets 0 1 2 3 4 5 6 7 8 9 10 11 12 13 14 15 16 17 18 19 20 21 22 23 24	Weather

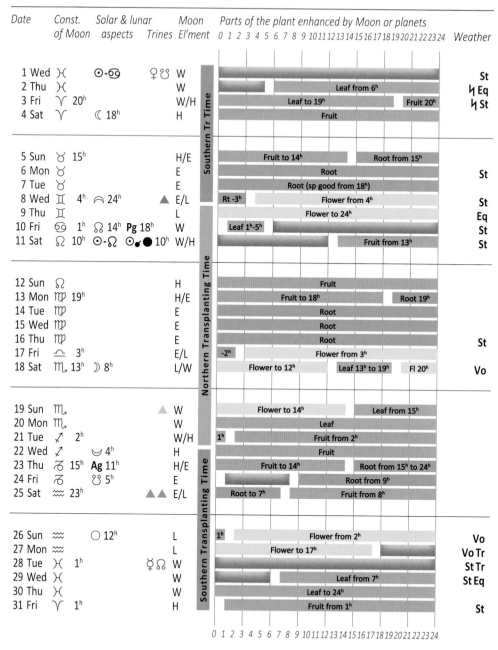

Southern Tr Time

Date	Const.	Aspects	Trines	El'ment	Parts of plant	Weather
1 Wed	♓	☉-♋	♀☋	W		St
2 Thu	♓			W	Leaf from 6ʰ	♄ Eq
3 Fri	♈ 20ʰ			W/H	Leaf to 19ʰ — Fruit 20ʰ	♄ St
4 Sat	♈	☾ 18ʰ		H	Fruit	
5 Sun	♉ 15ʰ			H/E	Fruit to 14ʰ — Root from 15ʰ	
6 Mon	♉			E	Root	St
7 Tue	♉			E	Root (sp good from 18ʰ)	
8 Wed	♊ 4ʰ	⌒ 24ʰ	▲	E/L	Rt -3ʰ — Flower from 4ʰ	St
9 Thu	♊			L	Flower to 24ʰ	Eq
10 Fri	♋ 1ʰ	☋ 14ʰ Pg 18ʰ		W	Leaf 1ʰ-5ʰ	St
11 Sat	♌ 10ʰ	☉-♌ ☉♂● 10ʰ		W/H	Fruit from 13ʰ	St

Northern Transplanting Time

Date	Const.	Aspects	Trines	El'ment	Parts of plant	Weather
12 Sun	♌			H	Fruit	
13 Mon	♍ 19ʰ			H/E	Fruit to 18ʰ — Root 19ʰ	
14 Tue	♍			E	Root	
15 Wed	♍			E	Root	
16 Thu	♍			E	Root	St
17 Fri	♎ 3ʰ			E/L	-2ʰ — Flower from 3ʰ	
18 Sat	♏ 13ʰ	☽ 8ʰ		L/W	Flower to 12ʰ — Leaf 13ʰ to 19ʰ — Fl 20ʰ	Vo
19 Sun	♏		▲	W	Flower to 14ʰ — Leaf from 15ʰ	
20 Mon	♏			W	Leaf	
21 Tue	♐ 2ʰ			W/H	1ʰ — Fruit from 2ʰ	
22 Wed	♐	⌣ 4ʰ		H	Fruit	
23 Thu	♑ 15ʰ	Ag 11ʰ		H/E	Fruit to 14ʰ — Root from 15ʰ to 24ʰ	
24 Fri	♑	☋ 5ʰ		E	Root from 9ʰ	
25 Sat	♒ 23ʰ		▲▲	E/L	Root to 7ʰ — Fruit from 8ʰ	

Southern Transplanting Time

Date	Const.	Aspects	Trines	El'ment	Parts of plant	Weather
26 Sun	♒	○ 12ʰ		L	1ʰ — Flower from 2ʰ	Vo
27 Mon	♒			L	Flower to 17ʰ	Vo Tr
28 Tue	♓ 1ʰ		☿♌	W		St Tr
29 Wed	♓			W	Leaf from 7ʰ	St Eq
30 Thu	♓			W	Leaf to 24ʰ	
31 Fri	♈ 1ʰ			H	Fruit from 1ʰ	St

0 1 2 3 4 5 6 7 8 9 10 11 12 13 14 15 16 17 18 19 20 21 22 23 24

Mercury ☿	Venus ♀	Mars ♂	Jupiter ♃	Saturn ♄	Uranus ♅	Neptune ♆	Pluto ♇
♌ 6 ♋	♍	♑ 24 ♐	♎	♐	♈	♒	♐
29 ♌ (R 19D)		30 ♑ (R 27D)		(R)	(7 R)	(R)	(R)

NB: All zodiac symbols refer to astronomical constellations, not astrological signs (see p. 26)

Planetary aspects

(**Bold** = *visible to naked eye*)

1 ♀☍ 17ʰ
2
3
4 ☾♂♁ 1ʰ ☾☍♃ 22ʰ

5
6
7
8 ♀△♂ 1ʰ ☾☍♄ 9ʰ
9 ☉♂☿ 2ʰ ☾☍♇ 11ʰ
10 ☾☍♂ 5ʰ
11 ☾♂☿ 4ʰ

12
13 ☽☍♅ 5ʰ
14 ☽♂♀ 18ʰ
15
16 ☽☍♁ 13ʰ
17 ☽♂♃ 13ʰ
18

19 ♃△♅ 9ʰ
20
21 ☽♂♄ 10ʰ
22 ☽♂♇ 19ʰ
23 ☽♂♂ 14ʰ
24 ☽☍☿ 20ʰ
25 ☉△♁ 17ʰ ☉△♄ 22ʰ

26
27 ☾♂♅ 12ʰ
28 ☿☍♌ 18ʰ
29
30 ☾☍♀ 11ʰ
31 ☾♂♁ 6ʰ

Warmth and Light aspects predominate this month and it is only the 'deviants' Mercury and Venus, which counterbalance this to some extent.

Northern Transplanting Time
Aug 9 2ʰ to Aug 22 2ʰ
Southern Transplanting Time
July 26 to Aug 8 22ʰ and
Aug 22 6ʰ to Sep 5

Harvest **seeds of fruit plants** and **grain** to be used for seed from Aug 11 13ʰ to Aug 13 18ʰ, and at other Fruit times, avoiding unfavourable times.

Immediately after harvest, sow catch crops like lupins, phacelia, mustard or wild flax.

Seeds for leaf plants: harvest at Leaf times, specially in the second half of the month.

Seeds for flower plants: at Flower times, specially in the second half of the month.

Burn **fly papers** in the cow barn at Flower times.

Ants in the house: burn when the Moon is in Leo, Aug 11 13ʰ to Aug 13 18ʰ.

Biodynamic preparations (Maria Thun's tree log preparations): Cut larch and fill with chamomile and put it in the ground between August 29 23ʰ and Sep 18 16ʰ.

Aug

Planet (naked eye) visibility
Evening: Venus, Jupiter
All night: Mars, Saturn
Morning: Mercury (from 20th)

Unfavourable time   47

September 2018

Date	Const. of Moon	Solar & lunar aspects	Trines	Moon El'ment	Parts of the plant enhanced by Moon or planets	Weather

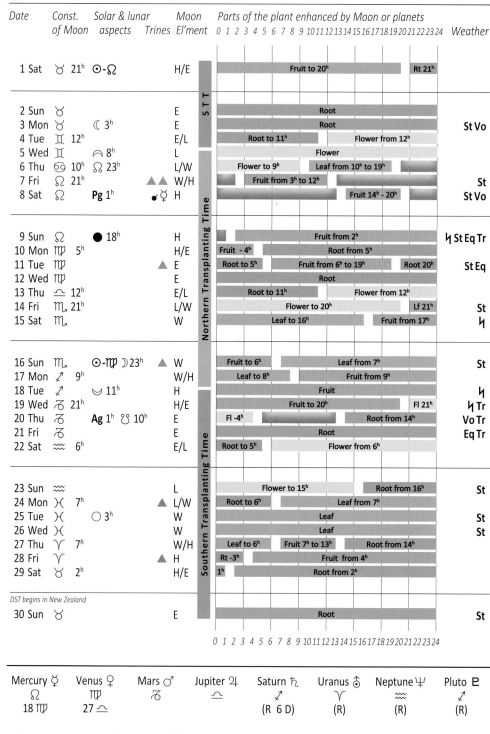

Parts of the plant enhanced by Moon or planets — scale 0 1 2 3 4 5 6 7 8 9 10 11 12 13 14 15 16 17 18 19 20 21 22 23 24

- 1 Sat — ♉ 21ʰ — ☉-♌ — H/E — Fruit to 20ʰ — Rt 21ʰ
- 2 Sun — ♉ — — E — Root
- 3 Mon — ♉ — ☾ 3ʰ — E — Root — St Vo
- 4 Tue — ♊ 12ʰ — — E/L — Root to 11ʰ — Flower from 12ʰ
- 5 Wed — ♊ — ⌒ 8ʰ — L — Flower
- 6 Thu — ♋ 10ʰ — ♌ 23ʰ — L/W — Flower to 9ʰ — Leaf from 10ʰ to 19ʰ
- 7 Fri — ♌ 21ʰ — ▲▲ — W/H — Fruit from 3ʰ to 12ʰ — St
- 8 Sat — ♌ — Pg 1ʰ — ●☿ — H — Fruit 14ʰ - 20ʰ — St Vo

(STT)

- 9 Sun — ♌ — ● 18ʰ — H — Fruit from 2ʰ — ♄ St Eq Tr
- 10 Mon — ♍ 5ʰ — — H/E — Fruit - 4ʰ — Root from 5ʰ
- 11 Tue — ♍ — ▲ — E — Root to 5ʰ — Fruit from 6ʰ to 19ʰ — Root 20ʰ — St Eq
- 12 Wed — ♍ — — E — Root
- 13 Thu — ♎ 12ʰ — — E/L — Root to 11ʰ — Flower from 12ʰ
- 14 Fri — ♏ 21ʰ — — L/W — Flower to 20ʰ — Lf 21ʰ — St
- 15 Sat — ♏ — — W — Leaf to 16ʰ — Fruit from 17ʰ — ♄

(Northern Transplanting Time)

- 16 Sun — ♏ — ☉-♍ ☽23ʰ — ▲ W — Fruit to 6ʰ — Leaf from 7ʰ — St
- 17 Mon — ♐ 9ʰ — — W/H — Leaf to 8ʰ — Fruit from 9ʰ
- 18 Tue — ♐ — ↄ 11ʰ — H — Fruit — ♄
- 19 Wed — ♑ 21ʰ — — H/E — Fruit to 20ʰ — Fl 21ʰ — ♄ Tr
- 20 Thu — ♑ — Ag 1ʰ ☊ 10ʰ — E — Fl -4ʰ — Root from 14ʰ — Vo Tr
- 21 Fri — ♑ — — E — Root — Eq Tr
- 22 Sat — ♒ 6ʰ — — E/L — Root to 5ʰ — Flower from 6ʰ

- 23 Sun — ♒ — — L — Flower to 15ʰ — Root from 16ʰ — St
- 24 Mon — ♓ 7ʰ — ▲ — L/W — Root to 6ʰ — Leaf from 7ʰ
- 25 Tue — ♓ — ○ 3ʰ — W — Leaf — St
- 26 Wed — ♓ — — W — Leaf — St
- 27 Thu — ♈ 7ʰ — — W/H — Leaf to 6ʰ — Fruit 7ʰ to 13ʰ — Root from 14ʰ
- 28 Fri — ♈ — ▲ — H — Rt -3ʰ — Fruit from 4ʰ
- 29 Sat — ♉ 2ʰ — — H/E — 1ʰ — Root from 2ʰ

(Southern Transplanting Time)

DST begins in New Zealand

- 30 Sun — ♉ — — E — Root — St

scale 0 1 2 3 4 5 6 7 8 9 10 11 12 13 14 15 16 17 18 19 20 21 22 23 24

Mercury ☿	Venus ♀	Mars ♂	Jupiter ♃	Saturn ♄	Uranus ♅	Neptune ♆	Pluto ♇
♌	♍	♑	♎	♐	♈	♒	♐
18 ♍	27 ♎			(R 6 D)	(R)	(R)	(R)

NB: All zodiac symbols refer to astronomical constellations, not astrological signs (see p. 26)

Planetary aspects
  (**Bold** = *visible to naked eye*)

September 2018

1 ☾ ☍ ♃ 9ʰ

2

3

4 ☾ ☍ ♄ 16ʰ

5 ☾ ☍ ♇ 20ʰ

6 ☾ ☍ ♂ 13ʰ

7 ☿ △ ♁ 8ʰ   ☿ △ ♄ 12ʰ   ☉ ☍ ♆ 18ʰ

8 **☾ ● ☿ 23ʰ**

9 ☾ ☍ ♆ 15ʰ

10

11 ☉ △ ♇ 15ʰ

12 ♀ ☍ ♁ 9ʰ   ☽ ☍ ♁ 22ʰ   ☽ ☌ ♀ 23ʰ

13

14 ☿ ☍ ♆ 2ʰ   ☽ ☌ ♃ 5ʰ

15

16 ☿ △ ♇ 3ʰ

17 ☽ ☌ ♄ 16ʰ

18

19 ☽ ☌ ♇ 1ʰ

20 ☽ ☌ ♂ 4ʰ

21 ☉ ☌ ☿ 2ʰ

22

23 ☽ ☌ ♆ 17ʰ

24 ☿ △ ♂ 2ʰ

25 ☾ ☍ ☿ 10ʰ

26

27 ☾ ☌ ♁ 10ʰ

28 ☉ △ ♂ 0ʰ   ☾ ☍ ♀ 1ʰ   ☾ ☍ ♃ 23ʰ

29

30

The constellations of Uranus, Saturn and Mercury suggest a warm start to September. They are supported by four Warmth trines. In the second half of the month Mars and (in the last week) Mercury focus on Earth qualities. This means a good harvest of root crops like potatoes, carrots and turnips can be expected.

Northern Transplanting Time
Sep 5 10ʰ to Sep 18 9ʰ
Southern Transplanting Time
Aug 22 to Sep 5 6ʰ and
Sep 18 13ʰ to Oct 2

The times recommended for the **fruit harvest** are those in which the Moon is in Aries or Sagittarius (Sep 17 9ʰ to Sep 19 20ʰ, Sep 27 7ʰ to 13ʰ, and Sep 28 4ʰ to Sep 29 1ʰ) or other Fruit times.

The harvest of **root crops** is always best undertaken at Root times. Storage trials of onions, carrots, beetroot and potatoes have demonstrated this time and again.

Good times for **sowing winter grain** are when the Moon is in Leo or Sagittarius (Sep 8 14ʰ to Sep 10 4ʰ, and Sep 17 9ʰ to Sep 19 20ʰ) avoiding unfavourable times, and at other Fruit times.

Rye can if necessary also be sown at Root times with all subsequent cultivations being carried out at Fruit times.

Control slugs by burning between Sep 6 10ʰ and 19ʰ.

Biodynamic preparations (Maria Thun's tree log preparations): Cut larch and fill with chamomile and put it in the ground between August 29 23ʰ and Sep 18 16ʰ.

Sep

Planet (naked eye) visibility
Evening: Venus (to 25th), Jupiter, Saturn
All night: Mars
Morning: Mercury (to 11th)

Unfavourable time   49

October 2018

All times in GMT

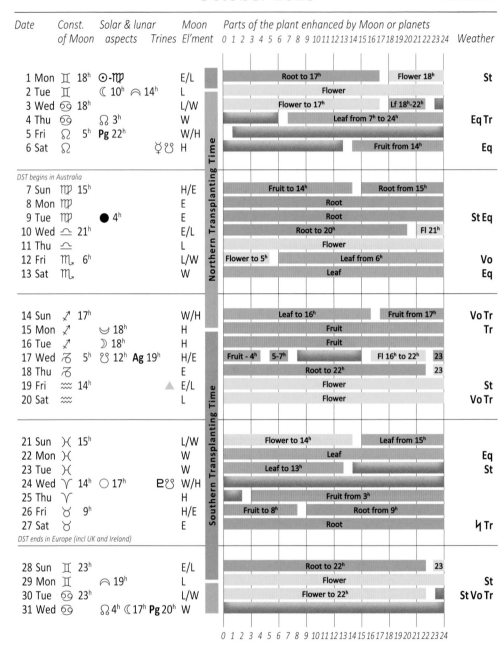

Date	Const. of Moon	Solar & lunar aspects	Trines	Moon El'ment	Parts of the plant enhanced by Moon or planets (0–24)	Weather
1 Mon	♊ 18^h	☉-♍		E/L	Root to 17^h; Flower 18^h	St
2 Tue	♊	☾ 10^h ⋒ 14^h		L	Flower	
3 Wed	♋ 18^h			L/W	Flower to 17^h; Lf 18^h-22^h	
4 Thu	♋	☊ 3^h		W	Leaf from 7^h to 24^h	Eq Tr
5 Fri	♌ 5^h	Pg 22^h		W/H		
6 Sat	♌		☿☋	H	Fruit from 14^h	Eq
DST begins in Australia						
7 Sun	♍ 15^h			H/E	Fruit to 14^h; Root from 15^h	
8 Mon	♍			E	Root	
9 Tue	♍	● 4^h		E	Root	St Eq
10 Wed	♎ 21^h			E/L	Root to 20^h; Fl 21^h	
11 Thu	♎			L	Flower	
12 Fri	♏ 6^h			L/W	Flower to 5^h; Leaf from 6^h	Vo
13 Sat	♏			W	Leaf	Eq
14 Sun	♐ 17^h			W/H	Leaf to 16^h; Fruit from 17^h	Vo Tr
15 Mon	♐	◡ 18^h		H	Fruit	Tr
16 Tue	♐	☽ 18^h		H	Fruit	
17 Wed	♑ 5^h	☋ 12^h Ag 19^h		H/E	Fruit - 4^h; 5-7^h; Fl 16^h to 22^h; 23	
18 Thu	♑			E	Root to 22^h; 23	
19 Fri	♒ 14^h		▲	E/L	Flower	St
20 Sat	♒			L	Flower	Vo Tr
21 Sun	♓ 15^h			L/W	Flower to 14^h; Leaf from 15^h	
22 Mon	♓			W	Leaf	Eq
23 Tue	♓			W	Leaf to 13^h	St
24 Wed	♈ 14^h	○ 17^h	♇☋	W/H		
25 Thu	♈			H	Fruit from 3^h	
26 Fri	♉ 9^h			H/E	Fruit to 8^h; Root from 9^h	
27 Sat	♉			E	Root	ɥ Tr
DST ends in Europe (incl UK and Ireland)						
28 Sun	♊ 23^h			E/L	Root to 22^h; 23	
29 Mon	♊	⋒ 19^h		L	Flower	St
30 Tue	♋ 23^h			L/W	Flower to 22^h	St Vo Tr
31 Wed	♋	☊ 4^h ☾ 17^h Pg 20^h		W		

Northern Transplanting Time

Southern Transplanting Time

Mercury ☿	Venus ♀	Mars ♂	Jupiter ♃	Saturn ♄	Uranus ⛢	Neptune ♆	Pluto ♇
♍ 16 ♎	♎ 13 ♍	♑	♎	♐	♈	♒	♐
29 ♏	(5 R)		28 ♏		(R)	(R)	(R 1 D)

NB: All zodiac symbols refer to astronomical constellations, not astrological signs *(see p. 26)*

Planetary aspects
*(**Bold** = visible to naked eye)*

October 2018

1	☽ ☌ ♄ 23ʰ
2	
3	☽ ☌ ♇ 2ʰ
4	☽ ☌ ♂ 10ʰ
5	
6	☿ ☋ 1ʰ ☽ ☌ ♆ 23ʰ
7	
8	
9	
10	☽ ☌ ☿ 5ʰ ☽ ☌ ☊ 6ʰ ☿ ☌ ☊ 18ʰ ☽ ☌ ♀ 22ʰ
11	☽ ☌ ♃ 23ʰ
12	
13	
14	
15	☽ ☌ ♄ 3ʰ ☿ ☌ ♀ 20ʰ
16	☽ ☌ ♇ 9ʰ
17	
18	☽ ☌ ♂ 12ʰ
19	☿ △ ♆ 10ʰ
20	
21	☽ ☌ ♆ 0ʰ
22	
23	
24	☉ ☍ ☊ 1ʰ ♇ ☋ 14ʰ ☽ ☌ ☊ 16ʰ ☽ ☌ ♀ 22ʰ
25	
26	☽ ☌ ☿ 9ʰ ☉ ☌ ♀ 14ʰ ☽ ☌ ♃ 14ʰ
27	
28	
29	☽ ☌ ♄ 8ʰ ☿ ☌ ♃ 11ʰ
30	☽ ☌ ♇ 7ʰ
31	♀ ☍ ☊ 9ʰ

October will be very changeable, and at the end of the month very rainy. This will help to restore some of the water reserves.

Northern Transplanting Time
Oct 2 16ʰ to Oct 15 16ʰ and
Oct 29 21ʰ to Nov 11
Southern Transplanting Time
Sep 18 to Oct 2 12ʰ and
Oct 15 20ʰ to Oct 29 17ʰ

Store fruit at any Fruit or Flower time outside transplanting time.

Harvest seeds of root plants at Root times, **seeds for leaf plants** at Leaf times, and **seeds for flower plants** at Flower times.

All **cleared ground** should be treated with compost and sprayed with barrel preparation, and ploughed ready for winter.

Control slugs by burning between Oct 3 18ʰ and Oct 4 24ʰ.

Planet (naked eye) visibility
Evening: Mars, Jupiter, Saturn
All night:
Morning:

Unfavourable time

November 2018

Date	Const. of Moon	Solar & lunar aspects	Moon Trines	El'ment	Parts of the plant enhanced by Moon or planets	Weather

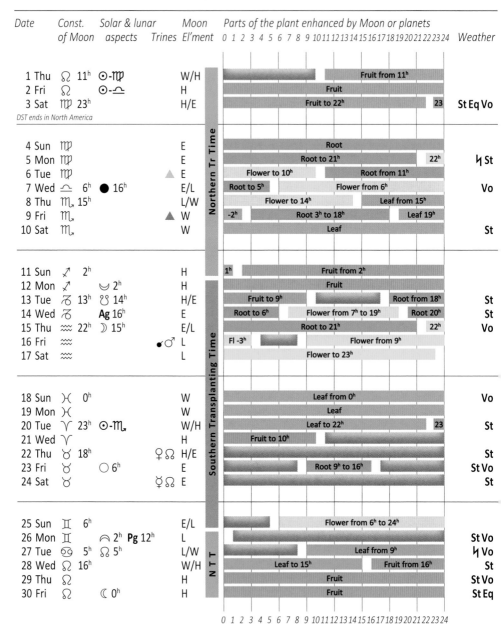

The main grid reads as follows:

Date	Const. of Moon	Solar & lunar aspects	Moon Trines	El'ment	Parts of the plant enhanced / times	Weather
1 Thu	♌ 11ʰ	☉-♍		W/H	Fruit from 11ʰ	
2 Fri	♌	☉-♎		H	Fruit	
3 Sat	♍ 23ʰ			H/E	Fruit to 22ʰ 23	St Eq Vo
DST ends in North America						
4 Sun	♍			E	Root	
5 Mon	♍			E	Root to 21ʰ 22ʰ	♄ St
6 Tue	♍		▲	E	Flower to 10ʰ Root from 11ʰ	
7 Wed	♎ 6ʰ	● 16ʰ		E/L	Root to 5ʰ Flower from 6ʰ	Vo
8 Thu	♏ 15ʰ			L/W	Flower to 14ʰ Leaf from 15ʰ	
9 Fri	♏		▲	W	-2ʰ Root 3ʰ to 18ʰ Leaf 19ʰ	
10 Sat	♏			W	Leaf	St
11 Sun	♐ 2ʰ			H	1ʰ Fruit from 2ʰ	
12 Mon	♐	☋ 2ʰ		H	Fruit	
13 Tue	♑ 13ʰ	☊ 14ʰ		H/E	Fruit to 9ʰ Root from 18ʰ	St
14 Wed	♑	Ag 16ʰ		E	Root to 6ʰ Flower from 7ʰ to 19ʰ Root 20ʰ	St
15 Thu	♒ 22ʰ	☽ 15ʰ		E/L	Root to 21ʰ 22ʰ	Vo
16 Fri	♒	●♂		L	Fl -3ʰ Flower from 9ʰ	
17 Sat	♒			L	Flower to 23ʰ	
18 Sun	♓ 0ʰ			W	Leaf from 0ʰ	Vo
19 Mon	♓			W	Leaf	
20 Tue	♈ 23ʰ	☉-♏		W/H	Leaf to 22ʰ 23	St
21 Wed	♈			H	Fruit to 10ʰ	
22 Thu	♉ 18ʰ	♀☊		H/E		St
23 Fri	♉	○ 6ʰ		E	Root 9ʰ to 16ʰ	St Vo
24 Sat	♉	☿☊		E		St
25 Sun	♊ 6ʰ			E/L	Flower from 6ʰ to 24ʰ	
26 Mon	♊	♉ 2ʰ **Pg** 12ʰ		L		St Vo
27 Tue	♋ 5ʰ	♌ 5ʰ		L/W	Leaf from 9ʰ	♄ Vo
28 Wed	♌ 16ʰ			W/H	Leaf to 15ʰ Fruit from 16ʰ	St
29 Thu	♌			H	Fruit	St Vo
30 Fri	♌	☾ 0ʰ		H	Fruit	St Eq

Left-side vertical labels: *Northern Tr Time*, *Southern Transplanting Time*, *N T T*

Bottom scale: 0 1 2 3 4 5 6 7 8 9 10 11 12 13 14 15 16 17 18 19 20 21 22 23 24

Mercury ☿	Venus ♀	Mars ♂	Jupiter ♃	Saturn ♄	Uranus ⛢	Neptune ♆	Pluto ♇
♏	♍	♑	♏	♐	♈ 15 ♓	♒	♐
(17 R)	(R 16 D)	10 ♒			(R)	(R 25 D)	

NB: All zodiac symbols refer to astronomical constellations, not astrological signs (see p. 26)

Planetary aspects
(**Bold** = *visible to naked eye*)

1	☽ ☌ ♂ 16ʰ
2	
3	☽ ☌ ♆ 6ʰ
4	
5	
6	☉ △ ♆ 7ʰ **☽ ☌ ♂ 9ʰ** ☽ ☍ ♁ 14ʰ
7	
8	☽ ☌ ♃ 20ʰ
9	☽ ☌ ☿ 15ʰ ♀ △ ♂ 16ʰ
10	
11	☽ ☌ ♄ 16ʰ
12	☽ ☌ ♇ 19ʰ
13	
14	
15	
16	**☽ ☌ ♂ 6ʰ**
17	☽ ☌ ♆ 9ʰ
18	
19	
20	☽ ☍ ♀ 17ʰ ☽ ☌ ♁ 24ʰ
21	
22	♀ ☊ 20ʰ
23	☽ ☌ ♃ 11ʰ ☽ ☍ ☿ 22ʰ
24	☿ ☊ 17ʰ
25	☽ ☍ ♄ 20ʰ
26	☉ ☌ ♃ 7ʰ ☽ ☍ ♇ 16ʰ
27	☉ ☌ ☿ 10ʰ ☿ ☌ ♃ 23ʰ
28	
29	
30	☽ ☍ ♂ 3ʰ ☽ ☍ ♆ 12ʰ

As October ends, so November begins with more rain. With the Earth constellations of Mars and Uranus there should be some good opportunities for autumn soil cultivations.

Northern Transplanting Time
Oct 29 to Nov 11 24ʰ
Nov 26 4ʰ to Dec 9
Southern Transplanting Time
Nov 12 4ʰ to Nov 25 24ʰ

The Flower times in Transplanting Time are ideal for **planting flower bulbs,** showing vigorous growth and vivid colours. The remaining Flower times should only be considered as back up, as bulbs planted on those times will not flower so freely.

If not already completed in October, all organic waste materials should be gathered and made into a **compost.** Applying the biodynamic preparations to the compost will ensure a rapid transformation and good fungal development. An application of barrel preparation will also help the composting process.

Fruit and forest trees will also benefit at this time from a spraying of horn manure and/or barrel preparation when being transplanted.

Best times for **cutting Advent greenery** and **Christmas trees** for transporting are Flower times outside Transplanting Time (Nov 14 7ʰ to 19ʰ, Nov 15 22ʰ to Nov 17 23ʰ and Nov 25 6ʰ to 24ʰ, avoiding unfavourable times).

Burn **fly papers** in cow barn at Flower times.

Planet (naked eye) visibility
Evening: Mars, Jupiter (to 5th), Saturn
All night:
Morning: Venus (from 2nd)

Nov

Unfavourable time   53

December 2018

All times in GMT

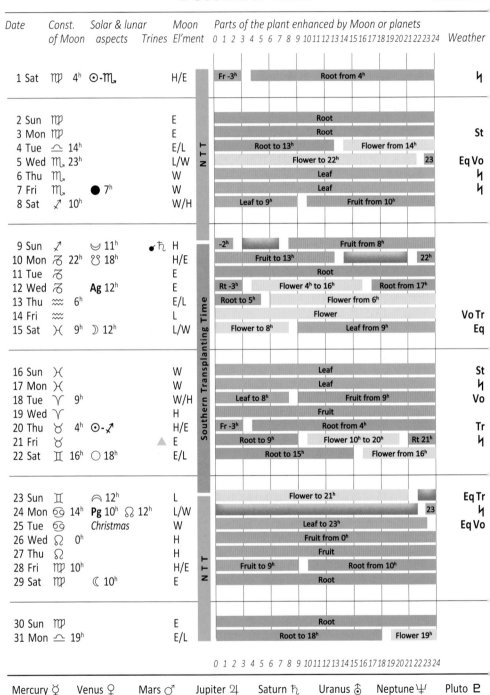

Date	Const. of Moon	Solar & lunar aspects	Moon Trines	El'ment	Parts of the plant enhanced by Moon or planets	Weather
1 Sat	♍ 4ʰ	☉-♏		H/E	Fr -3ʰ Root from 4ʰ	♄
2 Sun	♍			E	Root	
3 Mon	♍			E	Root	St
4 Tue	♎ 14ʰ			E/L	Root to 13ʰ Flower from 14ʰ	
5 Wed	♏ 23ʰ			L/W	Flower to 22ʰ 23	Eq Vo
6 Thu	♏			W	Leaf	♄
7 Fri	♏	● 7ʰ		W	Leaf	♄
8 Sat	♐ 10ʰ			W/H	Leaf to 9ʰ Fruit from 10ʰ	
9 Sun	♐	♄ 11ʰ	•♄	H	-2ʰ Fruit from 8ʰ	
10 Mon	♑ 22ʰ	☌ 18ʰ		H/E	Fruit to 13ʰ 22ʰ	
11 Tue	♑			E	Root	
12 Wed	♑	Ag 12ʰ		E	Rt -3ʰ Flower 4ʰ to 16ʰ Root from 17ʰ	
13 Thu	♒ 6ʰ			E/L	Root to 5ʰ Flower from 6ʰ	
14 Fri	♒			L	Flower	Vo Tr
15 Sat	♓ 9ʰ	☽ 12ʰ		L/W	Flower to 8ʰ Leaf from 9ʰ	Eq
16 Sun	♓			W	Leaf	St
17 Mon	♓			W	Leaf	♄
18 Tue	♈ 9ʰ			W/H	Leaf to 8ʰ Fruit from 9ʰ	Vo
19 Wed	♈			H	Fruit	Tr
20 Thu	♉ 4ʰ	☉-♐		H/E	Fr -3ʰ Root from 4ʰ	
21 Fri	♉		▲	E	Root to 9ʰ Flower 10ʰ to 20ʰ Rt 21ʰ	♄
22 Sat	♊ 16ʰ	○ 18ʰ		E/L	Root to 15ʰ Flower from 16ʰ	
23 Sun	♊	⌢ 12ʰ		L	Flower to 21ʰ	Eq Tr
24 Mon	♋ 14ʰ	Pg 10ʰ ☍ 12ʰ		L/W	23	♄
25 Tue	♋	Christmas		W	Leaf to 23ʰ	Eq Vo
26 Wed	♌ 0ʰ			H	Fruit from 0ʰ	
27 Thu	♌			H	Fruit	
28 Fri	♍ 10ʰ			H/E	Fruit to 9ʰ Root from 10ʰ	
29 Sat	♍	☾ 10ʰ		E	Root	
30 Sun	♍			E	Root	
31 Mon	♎ 19ʰ			E/L	Root to 18ʰ Flower 19ʰ	

Northern Transplanting Time (NTT) / *Southern Transplanting Time*

0 1 2 3 4 5 6 7 8 9 10 11 12 13 14 15 16 17 18 19 20 21 22 23 24

Mercury ☿	Venus ♀	Mars ♂	Jupiter ♃	Saturn ♄	Uranus ♅	Neptune ♆	Pluto ♇
♏ 4 ♎	♍	♒	♏	♐	♓	♒	♐
9 ♏ (R 6D)	16 ♎	19 ♓			(R)		

NB: All zodiac symbols refer to astronomical constellations, not astrological signs (see p. 26)

Planetary aspects

(**Bold** = *visible to naked eye)*

1 ♀☍♅ 3^h

2

3 ☾☍♅ 19^h **☾☌♀ 22^h**

4

5 **☾☌☿ 23^h**

6 ☾☌♃ 16^h

7 ♂☌♆ 15^h

8

9 **☽●♄ 6^h**

10 ☽☌♇ 4^h

11

12

13

14 ☽☌♆ 18^h

15 **☾☌♂ 3^h**

16

17

18 ☽☌♅ 8^h

19 ☽☍♀ 8^h

20

21 ☽☍☿ 7^h ☽☍♃ 8^h ♀△♆ 18^h **☿☌♃ 19^h**

22

23 ☾☍♄ 10^h

24 ☾☍♇ 2^h

25

26

27 ☾☍♆ 18^h

28 ☾☍♂ 17^h

29

30 ☾☍♅ 24^h

31

Planet (naked eye) visibility

Evening: Mars, Saturn (to 16th)

All night:

Morning: Mercury (from 3rd), Venus, Jupiter (from 11th)

December 2018

The December aspects offer little hope of true winter conditions arriving. Although the Light and Warmth aspects are modified by Water aspects, we need to reckon with many pests surviving to the spring. But perhaps the Light aspects will take the upper hand and produce clear, cold nights.

Northern Transplanting Time
Nov 26 to Dec 9 9^h and
Dec 23 14^h to Jan 5
Southern Transplanting Time
Dec 9 13^h to Dec 23 10^h

The transplanting time is good for **pruning trees and hedges.** Fruit trees should be pruned at Fruit or Flower times.

Best times for cutting **Advent greenery** and **Christmas trees** are at Flower times to ensure lasting fragrance.

The time for burning feathers or skins of **warm blooded pests** will only be in January 2019.

Southern hemisphere:
Harvest time for seeds (always avoiding unfavourable times):
Leaf seeds: Leaf times.
Fruit seeds: Fruit times, preferably with Moon in Leo (Dec 26 0^h to Dec 28 9^h).
Root seeds: Dec 28 10^h to Dec 31 18^h, and at other Root times.
Flower seeds: Dec 22 16^h to Dec 23 21^h, and at other Flower times.

Control slugs Dec 24 23^h to Dec 25 23^h.

We wish all our readers a blessed Advent and Christmastide and the best of health for the New Year of 2019

Sowing times for trees and shrubs

April 17: Pear, Birch, Lime tree, Robinia, Willow, Juniper, Plum, Hornbeam

May 26: Apple, Beech, Ash, Sweet chestnut, Alder, Larch, Lime tree, Elm, Thuja, Juniper, Plum, Hornbeam

June 6: Birch, Pear, Lime tree, Robinia, Willow, Thuja, Juniper, Plum, Hornbeam

June 16 to 15^h: Alder, Larch, Lime tree, Elm, Thuja, Juniper, Plum, Hornbeam

June 23: Alder, Larch, Lime tree, Elm, Juniper, Plum

June 27: Ash, Cedar, Fir, Spruce, Hazel Lime tree, Elm, Thuja, Juniper, Plum, Hornbeam

July 12: Ash, Cedar, Fir, Spruce, Hazel

Sep 12: Birch, Pear, Lime tree, Robinia, Willow, Thuja, Juniper, Plum, Hornbeam

Oct 10: Alder, Larch, Lime tree, Elm

Oct 24: Ash, Spruce, Hazel, Fir, Cedar

The above dates refer to sowing times of the seeds. They are not times for transplanting already existing plants.

The dates given are based on planetary aspects, which create particularly favourable growing conditions for the species in question. For trees and shrubs not mentioned above, sow at an appropriate time of the Moon's position in the zodiac, depending on the part of the tree or shrub to be enhanced. Avoid unfavourable times.

Felling times for timber

March 1: Birch, Pear, Robinia, Willow, Maple, Apple, Copper beech, Sweet chestnut, Walnut

March 13: Alder, Larch, Lime tree, Elm, Birch, Pear, Robinia, Willow, Maple, Apple, Copper beech, Sweet chestnut, Walnut

June 21: Elm, Larch, Lime tree, Elm

July 5: Maple, Apple, Copper beech, Sweet chestnut, Walnut, Spruce, Hornbeam, Pine, Fir, Thuja, Cedar, Plum, Plum

July 8: Ash, Spruce, Hazel, Fir, Cedar

July 12: Birch, Pear, Larch, Lime tree, Robinia, Willow

Aug 25: Ash, Spruce, Hazel, Fir, Cedar

Sep 7 3^h to 13^h: Alder, Larch, Lime tree, Elm

Oct 19: Alder, Larch, Lime tree, Elm

Nov 6: Ash, Spruce, Hazel, Fir, Cedar

Dec 20: Apple, Copper beech, Sweet chestnut, Walnut Ash, Spruce, Hazel, Fir, Cedar

Those trees which are not listed should be felled during November and December at Flower times during the descending Moon period (transplanting time). Avoid unfavourable times.

Types of crop

Flower plants

artichoke
broccoli
flower bulbs
flowering ornamental shrubs
flowers
flowery herbs
rose
sunflower

Leaf plants

asparagus
Brussels sprouts
cabbage
cauliflower
celery
chard
chicory (endive)
Chinese cabbage (pe-tsai)
corn salad (lamb's lettuce)
crisphead (iceberg) lettuce
curly kale (green cabbage)
endive (chicory)
finocchio (Florence fennel)
green cabbage (curly kale)
iceberg (crisphead) lettuce
kohlrabi
lamb's lettuce (corn salad)
leaf herbs
leek
lettuce
pe-tsai (Chinese cabbage)
red cabbage
rhubarb
shallots
spinach

Root plants

beetroot
black (Spanish) salsify
carrot
celeriac
garlic
horseradish
Jerusalem artichoke
parsnip
potato
radish
red radish
root tubers
Spanish (black) salsify

Fruit plants

aubergine (eggplant)
bush bean
courgette (zucchini)
cucumber
eggplant (aubergine)
grains
lentil
maize
melon
paprika
pea
pumpkin (squash)
runner bean
soya
squash (pumpkin)
tomato
zucchini (courgette)

The care of bees

A colony of bees lives in its hive closed off from the outside world. For extra protection against harmful influences, the inside of the hive is sealed with propolis. The link with the wider surroundings is made by the bees that fly in and out of the hive.

To make good use of cosmic rhythms, the beekeeper needs to create the right conditions in much the same way as the gardener or farmer does with the plants. The gardener works the soil and in so doing allows cosmic forces to penetrate it via the air. These forces can then be taken up and used by the plants until the soil is next moved.

When the beekeeper opens up the hive, the sealing layer of propolis is broken. This creates a disturbance, as a result of which cosmic forces can enter and influence the life of the hive until the next intervention by the beekeeper. By this means the beekeeper can directly mediate cosmic forces to the bees.

It is not insignificant which forces of the universe are brought into play when the hive is opened. The beekeeper can consciously intervene by choosing days for working with the hive that will help the colony to develop and build up its food reserves. The bees will then reward the beekeeper by providing a portion of their harvest in the form of honey.

Earth-Root times can be selected for opening the hive if the bees need to do more building. Light-Flower times encourage brood activity and colony development. Warmth-Fruit times stimulate the collection of nectar. Water-Leaf times are unsuitable for working in the hive or for the removal and processing of honey.

Since the late 1970s the varroa mite has affected virtually every bee colony in Europe. Following a number of comparative trials we recommend burning and making an ash of the varroa mite in the usual way. After dynamising it for one hour, the ash should be put in a salt-cellar and sprinkled lightly between the combs. The ash should be made and sprinkled when the Sun and Moon are in Taurus (May/June).

Feeding bees in preparation for winter

The herbal teas recommended as supplements in the feeding of bees prior to winter are all plants that have proved their value over many years. Yarrow, chamomile, dandelion and valerian are made by pouring boiling water over the flowers, allowing them to brew for fifteen minutes and then straining them. Stinging nettle, horsetail and oak bark are placed in cold water, brought slowly to the boil and simmered for fifteen minutes. Three grams (1 tablespoon) of each dried herb and half a litre (½ quart) of the prepared teas is enough to produce 100 litres (25 gal) of liquid feed. This is a particularly important treatment in years when there are large amounts of honeydew.

Fungal problems

The function of fungus in nature is to break down dying organic materials. It appears amongst our crops when unripe manure compost or uncomposted animal by-products such as horn and bone meal are used but also when seeds are harvested during unfavourable constellations: according to Steiner, 'When Moon forces are working too strongly on the Earth ...'

Tea can be made from horsetail (*Equisetum arvense*) and sprayed on to the soil where affected plants are growing. This draws the fungal level back down into the ground where it belongs.

The plants can be strengthened by spraying stinging nettle tea on the leaves. This will promote good assimilation, stimulate the flow of sap and help fungal diseases to disappear.

Biodynamic preparation plants

Pick **dandelions** in the morning at Flower times as soon as they are open and while the centre of the flowers are still tightly packed.

Pick **yarrow** at Fruit times when the Sun is in Leo (around the middle of August).

Pick **chamomile** at Flower times just before midsummer. If they are harvested too late, seeds will begin to form and there are often grubs in the hollow heads.

Collect **stinging nettles** when the first flowers are opening, usually around midsummer. Harvest the whole plants without roots at Flower times.

Pick **valerian** at Flower times around midsummer.

All the flowers (except valerian) should be laid out on paper and dried in the shade.

Collect **oak bark** at Root times. The pithy material below the bark should not be used.

Moon diagrams

The diagrams overleaf show for each month the daily position (evenings GMT) of the Moon against the stars and other planets. For viewing in the southern hemisphere, turn the diagrams upside down.

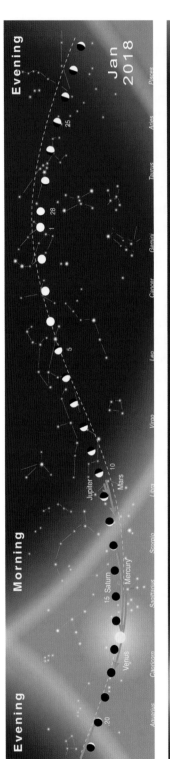

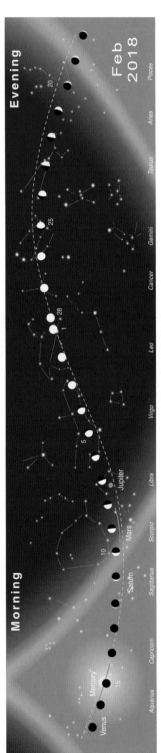

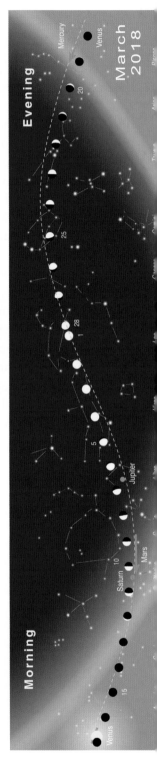

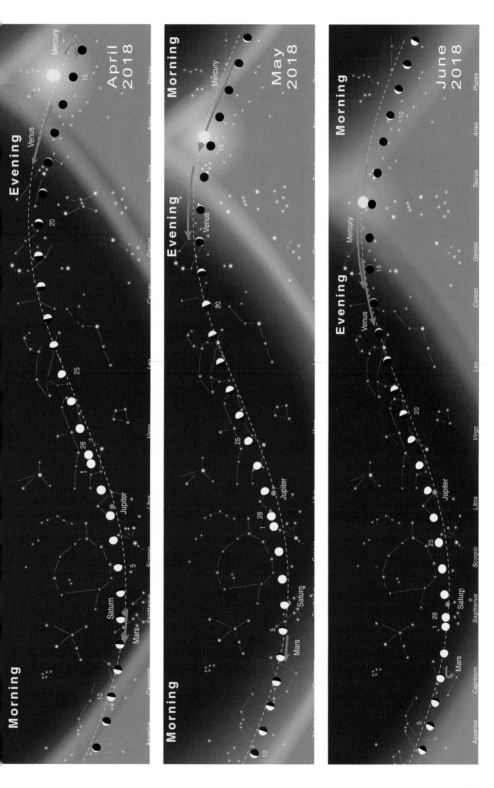

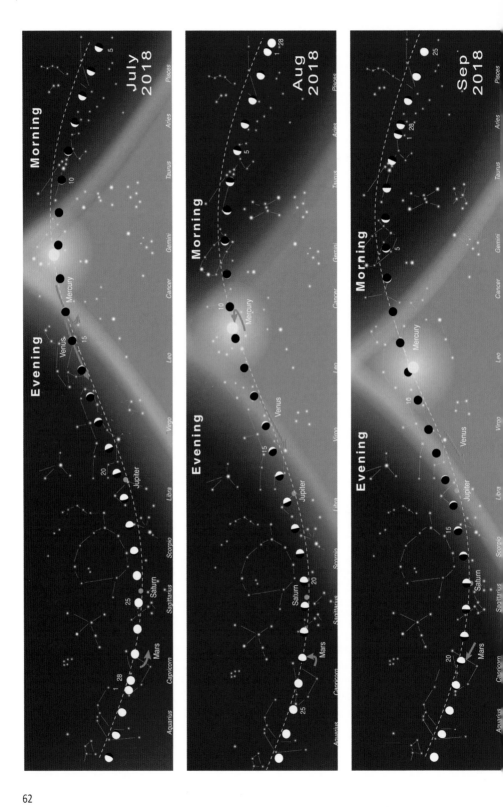

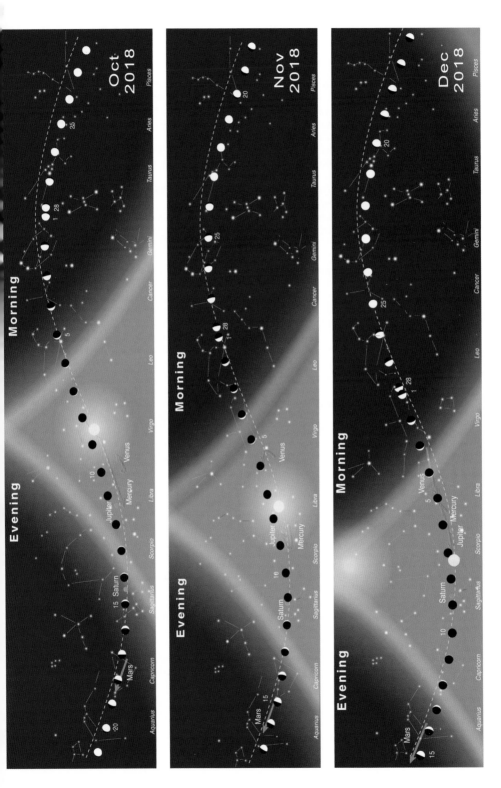

Oct 2018
Nov 2018
Dec 2018

Further Reading

Colquhoun, Margaret and Axel Ewald, *New Eyes for Plants,* Hawthorn

Karlsson, Britt and Per, *Biodynamic, Organic and Natural Winemaking,* Floris

Keyserlink, Adelbert Count von, *The Birth of a New Agriculture,* Temple Lodge

—, *Developing Biodynamic Agriculture,* Temple Lodge

Klett, Manfred, *Principles of Biodynamic Spray and Compost Preparations,* Floris

Koepf, H.H., *Koepf's Practical Biodynamics: Soil, Compost, Sprays and Food Quality,* Floris

Kranich, Ernst Michael, *Planetary Influences upon Plants,* Biodynamic Association, USA

Lepetit, Antoine, *What's so Special About Biodynamic Wine?* Floris

Masson, Pierre, *A Biodynamic Manual,* Floris

Morrow, Joel, *Vegetable Gardening for Organic and Biodynamic Growers,* Lindisfarne

Osthaus, Karl-Ernst, *The Biodynamic Farm,* Floris

Pfeiffer, Ehrenfried, *The Earth's Face,* Lanthorn

—, *Pfeiffer's Introduction to Biodynamics,* Floris

—, *Weeds and What They Tell Us,* Floris

—, & Michael Maltas, *The Biodynamic Orchard Book,* Floris

Philbrick, John and Helen, *Gardening for Health and Nutrition,* Steinerbooks, USA

Philbrick, Helen & Gregg, Richard B., *Companion Plants and How to Use Them,* Floris

Sattler, Friedrich & Eckard von Wistinghausen, *Growing Biodynamic Crops,* Floris

Schilthuis, Willy, *Biodynamic Agriculture,* Floris

Steiner, Rudolf, *Agriculture (A Course of Eight Lectures),* Biodynamic Association, USA

—, *Agriculture: An Introductory Reader,* Steiner Press, UK

—, *What is Biodynamics? A Way to Heal and Revitalize the Earth,* SteinerBooks, USA

Storl, Wolf, *Culture and Horticulture,* North Atlantic Books, USA

Thun, Maria, *Gardening for Life,* Hawthorn

—, *The Biodynamic Year,* Temple Lodge

Thun, Matthias, *When Wine Tastes Best: A Biodynamic Calendar for Wine Drinkers,* (annual) Floris

Waldin, Monty, *Monty Waldin's Best Biodynamic Wines,* Floris

Weiler, Michael, *Bees and Honey, from Flower to Jar,* Floris

Wright, Hilary, *Biodynamic Gardening for Health and Taste,* Floris

Biodynamic Associations

Demeter International
www.demeter.net
Australia:
Bio-Dynamic Research Institute
www.demeter.org.au
Biodynamic Agriculture Australia
www.biodynamics.net.au
Canada: Society for Bio-Dynamic Farming & Gardening in Ontario
biodynamics.on.ca
India: Bio-Dynamic Association of India (BDAI)
www.biodynamics.in

New Zealand:
Biodynamic Association
www.biodynamic.org.nz
South Africa: Biodynamic Agricultural Association of Southern Africa
www.bdaasa.org.za
UK: Biodynamic Association
www.biodynamic.org.uk
USA: Biodynamic Association
www.biodynamics.com